Paris 1935

Jean Follain (1903–71) was born in Canisy, Normandy. After studying law at Caen, he worked as a judge while pursuing a literary career. He published several poetry collections, including *Exister* (1947) and *Espaces d'instants* (1971), as well as prose works about places, *Paris* (1935), *Canisy* (1942) and *Chef-lieu* (1950). Follain knew Éluard and Aragon and was a close friend of Max Jacob. He is often linked with the descriptive, philosophical poets Francis Ponge, Eugène Guillevic and Philippe Jaccottet.

Kathleen Shields taught English at French universities (Paris and Caen) and worked on large bilingual dictionary projects in France and England. For many years she lectured in French at Maynooth University, where she specialised in teaching translation. She is the author of publications in translation studies and literature and of review essays in the *Dublin Review of Books*. She lives in Dublin.

JEAN FOLLAIN

Paris 1935

Translated by Kathleen Shields

Cover photograph: *Self-portrait at the Window*, 1935,
by Dora Maar (1907–97) – photographer, painter, Surrealist, activist,
and teacher and lover of Picasso, whom she met
in the winter of 1935–6

© ADAGP, Paris and DACS, London 2023
Silver gelatin contact print
Courtesy Huxley-Parlour Gallery, London

,

First published in Great Britain in 2024
by CB editions
146 Percy Road London W12 9QL
www.cbeditions.com

Originally published in French as *Paris* in 1935
by Editions R.-A. Corrêa
© Editions Phébus, Paris, 2006

Translation © Kathleen Shields, 2024

The right of Kathleen Shields to be identified as translator
of this work has been identified in accordance with
Section 77 of the Copyright, Designs and Patents Act 1988

Printed and bound in the UK by Blissetts, Brentford, TW8 9EX

ISBN 978-1-7394212-3-6

Contents

Introduction

KATHLEEN SHIELDS

'I love the empty Paris of August days.' If cities are composed of millions of subjective geographies, then Follain's *Paris* gives us the impressions of a young man from Normandy as he observes the interactions and habitats of Parisians in the mid-1930s. These are short, elegiac, humorous and objectively lyrical chapters that fuse journalism, history and poetry. Their sensory richness gives the reader more than a camera-eye view: the tastes, smells, sounds, colours and weather of Paris at a time of great transition, where vestiges of the nineteenth century and pre-revolutionary times survive alongside the new high-rise purpose-built apartments on its fringe. This is a protean book, at the junction of description, narrative and scientific scrutiny. The walker-writer has been living in Paris for ten years and perceives contemporary people and events in the light of all of human, even non-human, history.

Scrupulously detached observation contrasts strikingly with lyrical empathy. Follain calls into question the shifting relationships between humans and their surroundings, avoiding metaphor and big romantic gestures. He is sometimes grouped with the poets of the object, Ponge and Guillevic, two philosophical, descriptive writers who emerged during the Second World War. It is often noted that his path of lyrical impersonality bypasses surrealism, although he counted Éluard as a friend and defended Aragon in a case against the publisher Gallimard. Yet, despite his avoidance of surrealist engagement, he is not aesthetically conservative.

When writers describe their wanderings in cities, they remember other writers who have gone before them and moved through the same spaces. One of the tutelary spirits in *Paris 1935* is Guillaume Apollinaire, a modernist who experimented with juxtaposition, collage and a radical absence of punctuation, all figures of style that feature in Follain's writing. The contrasting role model who appears in *Paris* is Balzac, the realist mapper of society and psychologies, in particular Balzac's protagonist Rastignac, an outsider who, like Follain himself, comes from the provinces to make his way in the capital. Like a novelist, Follain often switches from external description of the city to an empathetic point of view to present short story buds, snatches of lore, and oral histories of fellow citizens. He embraces his two forebears Balzac and Apollinaire with realist micro-narratives expressed in experimental lyrical prose.

A second tension exists between the human and the non-human. Follain's poetic universe is human but not human-centred. There are vertiginous leaps in scale, as the perspective shifts from the cosmic, to the human, right down to the microscopic: insects, moss, pollen, dust, builders' rubble, and leaf mould.

> On the Rue de Belleville, at a shop where a woman sells funeral wreaths, the window display has a little bicycle made of pearls, specially commissioned by the proud family of a racing cyclist in memory of the champion. An

intangible cloud of flour from the bakery next door floats around the little funerary bicycle.

In the same vein, the narrator notices the human craftsmanship that went into decorating the streetlamps but also spots the tiny dust particles that have settled on them, the same dust that gets into women's hair and the film of sweat on their skin. He records fleeting intimate human gestures 'that leave a small trace in the universe'.

Finally, there is the tension between the single human lifespan and all the generations that have shaped the city before. Towards the end of his career, in a lecture that he gave in Mannheim, Follain spoke about the central preoccupation of his work: 'what haunts me most is the very mystery of time, human time in dialogue, as it were, with the timespan of objects'. Timescales are superimposed: geological time, human and animal lifespans and the existence of microscopic particles and organisms. The 1930s city has evolved through revolutions, changes of regime and war, and survived attrition and destruction both natural and man-made. What does the future hold in store for it? 'Thousands of years hence will it be possible for a schoolchild to confuse the Place de la Concorde with the Hanging Gardens of Babylon?'

Jean Follain was a man marked by war. He was born in 1903 and spent his childhood in Canisy, in rural Normandy, near the town of Saint-Lô. When he was eleven the outbreak of the Great War divided his life into a before and an after, childhood and adulthood, leaving an indelible impression on him. The formative childhood world of traditional crafts and trades is celebrated in many of his poems and in his prose work about his village, *Canisy* (1942). In later adult life, he was badly shaken by the complete destruction of Saint-Lô by Allied bombing in 1944. In his prose work about Saint-Lô, *Chef-lieu* (1950), he writes that he was in Paris when a friend told him about this terrible event: 'A friend told me about the death of the departmental town. It was completely unrecognisable. The ability of things to endure has been definitively vanquished.'

Follain attended secondary school in Saint-Lô, where his father was a science teacher, and in 1921 went to Caen university to study law. While entertaining dreams of a literary career with his college friends he was also awarded prizes for his law studies and in 1924 moved to Paris, where he trained at a barrister's office while pursuing his literary ambitions. It was difficult at first. He had idealised the bohemian world of Montmartre and struggled to find a foothold as legal correspondent for various periodicals, but once he met and befriended the writers André Salmon, Pierre Mac Orlan, Max Jacob, Pierre Reverdy and Armen Lubin he found his place in the literary ecosystem. It is in *Paris 1935* that the three careers of poetry, law and journalism come together and find their expression for the first time.

Follain continued to work in the law until 1961, first as an *avocat* (barrister) in Paris until the end of 1952, then as a *magistrat* (judge) in Charleville, commuting by train to Paris. In 1934 he married the painter Madeleine Dinès. Although he had been exempted from military service in the 1920s because of poor eyesight, he was mobilised as a gunner in April 1940. In a letter to his friend, the sociologist Georges Duveau, he wrote, 'What kind of life lies before us? How will we find our old Paris again!!? [...] As the good people of my home place say, "we have to endure". So, let's endure.' He was discharged from the army in July 1940 at the Armistice and returned to Paris in October 1940, hoping to find legal work. The literary sphere became complex. He was awarded the *Prix Blumenthal* in 1940. Some of his friends and peers were in prison camps; others like Jean Paulhan were in the resistance, but Follain continued publishing in Paris through the war. Like some other anti-Vichy writers (even including Aragon and Paulhan), Follain kept up contact with the influential pro-German Drieu La Rochelle. His old friend Max Jacob died in Drancy in 1944. In the 1950s and 1960s, as committee member of the French section of the PEN Club, he undertook many trips throughout the world. In 1970 he was awarded the *Grand prix de poésie* by the Académie Française for the whole body of his work. He died in an accident in 1971 when he was knocked down by a car on the Quai des Tuileries as he was walking home from a dinner just after midnight.

Wandering, wayfaring, watching and listening, Follain's self-effacing *flâneur* is an unusual figure because the narrator's fellow citizens are women as often as men. They are secretaries, young widows with children, post-office workers, shop assistants, housewives, women working in the markets, waitresses, stockbrokers' wives, apprentices, skilled workers, country women from the provinces who have made a new home in Paris. Prostitutes and artists' models also feature. We see the aging artists' model who asks for extra milk in her coffee because she hasn't enough to eat, or the unmarried suburban post-office worker at home alone in the evenings. There is not always solidarity between women: older women office workers are portrayed being mean to their junior colleagues.

Follain's legal training leads him to present a broad cross-section of society and sometimes to focus on shocking examples of injustice and cruelty. Life is harsh to the woman history scholar who has become a figure of fun after her youth full of promise. In the Botanical Gardens a young woman hides inside the museum, trembling for fear that she will be found by her pimp searching for her in nearby streets, while in another part of the gardens old servant women who have been fired go to cry on the benches as the gardener and his assistants quietly rake the gravel. When the wanderer leaves a suburban cinema at four in the morning after watching beautiful screen heroines, the focus jumps to the film-star herself: 'sick and tired of jealous fits and brief flings, disgusted with flowers and gold vanity cases'. Women do not have the same freedom of movement about the city as men do.

> Many middle-class girls hide a life of passion secretly within themselves. [...] They struggle with men everywhere: in buses, on washroom staircases where hands with red hairs on them land on their shoulders, in quiet streets in Passy where sons of boorish gardeners still live.

Such anecdotes are unusual in the literature of city strolling. Evidence is presented while it is up to the reader to conclude.

Follain's book stands apart from the constellation of writings about cities that appeared in the early twentieth century. It would be a mistake to retrospectively read *Paris*

1935 through Walter Benjamin's concept of the *flâneur* as it has come to be understood in the English-speaking world. Follain's book was published after Aragon's surrealist *Paris Peasant* (1926) and is contemporaneous with Walter Benjamin's *Paris, Capital of the Nineteenth Century* (1935) but appeared before Benjamin's critique of commodification in *Paris of the Second Empire in Baudelaire* (1938). Walter Benjamin, in symptomatic readings of Baudelaire, inspired by Aragon's *Paris Peasant*, elevated the *flâneur* into an allegorical figure, the alienated (usually male) individual living under capitalism in the industrial age. The central section of his *Paris of the Second Empire in Baudelaire* presents the *flâneur* as a figure who embodies the problematic relationship between the individual and the crowd in the capitalist metropolis, a leisured boulevardier who does not work, at least not full time, and who has a heightened awareness of the commodification of human beings and their work.

Benjamin's *flâneur* has left an imprint on city writing right up to our own time. In English-language cultural theory he is also associated with solitary male sexuality and a certain kind of male gaze. Lauren Elkin develops this point about gender when she reclaims the city streets for women in 2016:

> The great writers of the city, the great psychogeographers, the ones you read about in the *Observer* on weekends: they are all men, and at any given moment you'll also find them writing about each other's work, creating a refined canon of masculine writer-walkers. As if a penis were a requisite walking appendage, like a cane.

While this statement may be true for our century's understanding of the *flâneur* it is not accurate for Follain's time. Indeed, not all city writers are men. Virginia Woolf was writing her essays about London 'street haunting' in the early 1930s, at the same time as Follain's *flâneur* was wandering the streets of Paris.

Loan words are often narrower in meaning than they are in their original language and the noun *flâneur*, shorn of its cognates, is no exception. Follain often uses the expression '*le flâneur*' as an impersonal way of presenting the narrator, instead of saying 'I', but I have decided not to use this term in my translation. The word can be limited and inert in English, perhaps even a little pretentious. Dickens, in his *Uncommercial Traveller*, differentiates between two kinds of walking: one is 'straight on end to a definite goal at a round pace' while the other is 'objectless, loitering, and purely vagabond'. In making this distinction he echoes French dictionary definitions of the verb *flâner*. Like many French authors of urban vignettes of the early nineteenth century, Follain uses this verb in its ordinary sense, to wander without a clear purpose or predetermined sense of direction. (The Irish or Scottish verbs *dander* and *stravague* capture the meaning of *flâner* in its everyday French use.) Apollinaire's short prose text about his time in Auteuil in 1912, *Le Flâneur des deux rives* (1918), is important in this respect since both Follain and Apollinaire see the *flâneur* (or *flâneuse*) as someone who likes wandering unhurriedly, taking in impressions, bumping into people. Whereas many city writers are detached, standing apart from the crowds that they describe, and observing others without being observed, Follain's impersonal narrator is a participant observer, both immersed and detached, passing on some of the stories that he has been told.

To be able to communicate great leaps in perspective, in space and in time, Follain has developed a unique prose style. The focus shifts from habitual practices to one-off events and from general statements to specific examples. The writing piles on more and more relative and prepositional clauses, so that the information within the sentence can be presented in an unexpected order, zoning in from the general to the particular within a single phrase or disconcertingly alternating between definite and indefinite articles and between singulars and plurals. The past tenses are more precise than in English and are used unexpectedly, indicating a one-off action where you would expect a habitual one, and vice versa. Past and present tenses can switch places within the same paragraph. Punctuation is minimal and sentence components are presented separated by commas, sometimes concluded with a colon before a list. I have kept as many of these unusual features as possible in English.

Follain repeatedly uses very precise technical terms from decorative arts and construction, from woodworking, jewellery making, tailoring, porcelain and glass manufacturing. Some artefacts recur as motifs, for instance the details of feathers, braid and embroidery on uniforms worn by soldiers, policemen, park attendants and circus performers, or the fluted shape of unbreakable café glassware. There is a richness of synonyms for different smells of cooking, vegetation, floral perfumes and damp, different sorts of bars or different types of woollen overcoats.

The whole of Paris is bathed in golds, ochres and yellows, and the reds, blacks and greys of evening light and storms. The material world of the city is perceived with an anthropologist's or an archaeologist's eye.

Paris 1935 offers insights into some of the major social changes of the time. It took a long time for France to recover from the carnage of the Great War but by the end of the 1920s the country was beginning to emerge from its period of mourning and memorialisation. Yet it seems that Jean Follain cannot forget the Great War of 1914 and the palpable absence of a missing generation of young men. His narrator sees young widows and their young children everywhere he goes, on public transport, in crowds, at funerals.

Inward migration to Paris from the countryside was significant. Many of the inhabitants of Paris that we encounter in this book are recent arrivals from all regions of France. A good number are from Brittany, some are fellow Normans, others are from the Aveyron, the Auvergne, the Luberon, the Berry. In 1914 approximately half of the population of France was living in the countryside, making a basic living from the land and related rural professions. This is the world of Follain's Norman childhood that he was to revisit so often in his poetry. But after the war the rural exodus increased to such an extent that by the 1931 census the number of people living in towns outnumbered those in the country for the first time.

Paris was also a magnet for immigrants from abroad. Follain mentions the markets in the suburbs where there are housewives of Spanish and Italian descent. The artists' models on the Left Bank come from everywhere, 'women from Paris, Marseilles and Toulouse, who have some Breton, gypsy, or even Irish blood in them'. There are Jewish salesmen at cafés and black artists in the nightclubs. Follain grew up during the time of the colonies when France represented itself radiating culture and civilisation throughout the world from the epicentre of Paris. He remembers an illustration in an encyclopedia from his childhood during the early Third Republic:

> The name and layout of the Place de la Concorde belong to that time when the map of French African colonies in the pastel-coloured atlas was decorated with an engraving depicting a naked, brown-skinned child sitting on an Arab's lap. This child was kissing a little white child who sat on the lap of a robed woman holding a tablet inscribed with the words Justice and Fraternity.

There is a touch of irony about the idealised vision belonging to 'that time'. Instead, what fascinates Follain in the present is the reality of diverse people on the ground.

Parisians themselves were to change under cosmopolitan and regional influences in music and food, whether they took to them enthusiastically, whether they resisted, or whether they created something new. Cities, forever changing, are a constant reminder that culture cannot be reduced to a clash between tradition and the modern. Jean Follain's *Paris 1935* shows startling contrasts of older ways of life, regional dress, ancient trades and horse-drawn vehicles, alongside new ones like the metro, buses, cars, and high-rise apartment buildings with running water, electricity and gas.

Nowhere are these contrasts more evident than in the

world of work. Follain is fascinated by very old trades, such as the craft of baking which he jokingly presents in heraldic terms, or the old butchering and dairying skills at the markets, but also by the material culture of the city created by all the small artisan workshops: glassware, gilding, the decorations on café ceramics, engraving, textiles. These specialist skills remind him of the Norman country trades and professions that he knew as a child. Although mechanisation and rationalisation had radically transformed work patterns in France in the 1920s in big industries such as car manufacturing, mining, ship building, steel and chemical production, these changes only affected a fifth of the workforce. Most workers were still employed in small firms and in 1931 a third of them still worked in traditional ways in firms of fewer than ten people. Follain celebrates artisans, men and women, but he also shows us policemen, civil servants, bank tellers, road menders, store delivery men. Two chapters are devoted to old professions, the law and the church. In others we see the harsh reality of different grades of prostitution and the grim poverty of bohemian life.

As the depression after the Wall Street crash began to bite from 1931, causing a sharp drop in the value of the franc, a surge in unemployment, reduced working hours and a loss of income and savings, a rising tide of xenophobia swept the country and immigrants were blamed. Herriot's centre-left government passed an immigration law in 1932, imposing quotas for non-naturalised industrial workers. The depression led to measures blocking women from administrative careers and they were actively discouraged from the professions. Across the political spectrum, left and right, the consensus was that it was better for women to stay in the home to rear children and leave jobs free for men. Yet at a time of hardship, poverty and sketchy social security women did not always have this option and had to live by their wits. Follain wonders about the prostitutes' child-care arrangements and shows those who are self-employed doing their laundry on days off from work when they can arrange to have their children beside them. The women's suffrage law was not passed in France until the end of 1944. The historian Eugen Weber sums up the position of women in the 1930s:

> So nothing is univocal, nothing is clear, except that women are not as good as men: second-class workers, second-class citizens. Recourse against that sentence was difficult since women had no vote, hence no access to political power, at least in its formal and most obvious form.

A chapter on street rioting gives a glimpse of just how heated politics in the city had become, with street activism and demonstrations (between right-wing leagues on the one hand and Communists and Socialists on the other) culminating in the violent clashes between the leagues and the police on 6 February 1934 that left seventeen people dead and many more injured. These events led to the alliance between the Communists, the Socialists and the Radical Party and their electoral victory with the Front Populaire in 1936. However, Follain sees these contemporary 'days of rioting' as a cultural practice that blurs into past street-fighting during the Commune, and his book presents Parisians not by their politics but through contrasts in social class, income and profession (by categories such as *petit bourgeois, artisan, bourgeois*). By temperament he views contemporary events through a sociological and anthropological rather than a political lens.

Before Follain even arrives in Paris the image of the city has already been imprinted firmly on his mind through reading novels, newspapers, maps and encyclopedias.

> It was in pictures in the *Petit Journal Illustré* that I first saw Paris. I remember a picture of the banquet that was given in 1900 for all the mayors of France; they were shown arriving at the banqueting hall, passing through double ranks of Republican Guards on either side; you could see a country mayor in a blue smock, a mayor who was also a parish priest, a mayor from Brittany in a braided coat, all of them wearing the tricolour sash.

The Paris of the universal exhibitions is a recurring theme, including the Universal Exhibition of 1889, the centenary year of the French Revolution, for which the Eiffel Tower was built. For someone born outside it, Paris is the most capital of all capital cities, the prestigious home of culture and centralised government.

But knowledge derived from books and newspapers is theoretical, linear, Cartesian knowledge. When you are on the ground the Paris earth breaks through the paving stones and 'the old woman with her stick and the beggar with his pouch will resist the dazzling, all-too-human glass and stone constructions that impose their geometry on the earth'. The second chapter is a map of the sentiments, an attempt to locate intangible moods and feelings triggered by the city in different weathers and times. Many of the inhabitants, narrator included, are shown walking home alone to their rooms late at night while by day the streets, bars, cafés and workplaces are bustling and teeming with life. Mapping is an attempt to put a shape on the wanderings and chance encounters, but this personal Paris is not an ordered controllable miniature world.

Follain is drawn to the hills of Paris: Chaillot, Montmartre, La Montagne Sainte-Geneviève, and especially working-class Belleville near the old hill of Chaumont. He returns again and again to the Rue des Envierges, a street in Belleville in the twentieth arrondissement that opens out on a high escarpment from which you can view the whole of Paris and the Eiffel Tower on the horizon. On the Fortifications at the edge of the city he takes out an old naval telescope and looks down on Paris, travelling back in time while imagining what might be happening in intimate spaces in the present. But a telescopic lens can only take you so far, you need to carry on in your imagination to experience the city from within.

> [He] located the green blur of the Buttes-Chaumont where the water is so still under the Suicides' Bridge. On the horizon in the opposite direction the fine structure of the Eiffel Tower reared up. [...] But the old naval spyglass left some things hidden at the heart and outer edges of Paris: Paris with its lilies, muck and gold, its inscriptions on columns, or mouldings on grey houses, its women at café terraces wearing hats decorated with sprigs and flowers, or the hand turning the doorknob, or the glove being taken off to reveal the hand when the evening newspapers appear.

Vertical travel to the heights of the city and observation with the scientific instrument of the telescope is not enough.

> Luna Park is full of rotten planks, worn grass and faded canvas; there's a whole flora there: spindly grasses, tiny mosses and minuscule mushrooms proliferate on the human attractions.

Sometimes, to understand a place, microscopic inspection is also required.

Follain is fascinated by the slopes of the Fortifications and the Zone, a liminal space between the countryside and the capital. During the July Monarchy in 1841 Louis-Philippe and his powerful minister Adolphe Thiers forced legislation through the Assembly to build a defensive wall around Paris, known as the Fortifications or the Thiers Wall, completed in 1846. Thirty-four kilometres long, with forty-five gates, the wall ran between one and three kilometres outside the city limits of that time. However, the Fortifications (or *les fortifs* as they came to be known) fell the first time they were tested, during the Prussian siege in the winter of 1870–71, and in 1919 the Chamber of Deputies voted to demolish them. Demolition, by pick and shovel, was not completed until the 1940s.

The green hilly area between Paris and the wall was exempt from city taxes (the *octroi*) and so wine was cheap here and over time many bars, dance halls and cafés sprang up, some of them depicted by Impressionist painters. Land was cheap here too, stimulating an influx of workers, small businesses and factories as the city expanded, leading to the development of the *petite banlieue* or 'little suburb'. Building was forbidden in the military defensible strip known as the *Zone non ædificandi*, a belt 250 metres outside the wall. When the Zone was abandoned by the army after the defeat of 1871 it did not remain empty for long as investors let out plots of land to squatters who built shacks and made their homes there.

A shanty town mushroomed around the edges of Paris and by 1920, 50,000 people lived in the Zone. Its inhabitants (known as *zoniers*, later pejoratively as *zonards*) were a third class of the non-respectable poor, neither skilled workers nor the bourgeoisie, and the Zone became an interstitial symbolic space, disordered and unhealthy, neither the city nor the country, condemned in newspapers and celebrated in popular song. Follain mentions some of its inhabitants, ragpickers, poor children, very young prostitutes, but also describes a man sitting outside his shack working on mathematical problems. He is drawn to the Fortifications and the Zone because they represent the city at its inception, in its messiest, most unpredictable form at the point where it begins both to emerge from and encroach on the countryside. Similarly, he devotes a closing chapter to the transitional space of the suburbs, crossed by bus or train, a place with villas and kitchen gardens, that is neither city nor country, where you can only speculate about what might be going on behind closed doors. 'The suburbs conceal private chapels and stolen or abused children.'

Follain's mind city shows the points where human constructions meet the natural world. He describes the Paris paving stones as being 'set' in their mossy surround (in the same way as a jeweller sets a stone in a ring). The displaced countryman is also curious about survivals of country customs, flora and fauna that can still be seen in the city. Although he was only thirty-two when *Paris 1935* was published, a sense of fleeting time pervades the book, in descriptions of old Second Empire café decors, the trades-people's enduring customs, popular entertainments such as theatres, circuses, funfairs and street singing, the ritual of liturgy and artefacts in churches, the ritual aperitifs in front of cafés. Time passes and human constructions are forgotten or repurposed or eroded.

Jean Follain was a reasonably well-known writer during his lifetime but since his death his work has largely been forgotten in France, except by the poet Jacques Réda, another city writer, and except for featuring in anthologies. When it appeared in 1935 Follain's *Paris* was well-received by critics and readers. It was his first book-length publication, launching his literary career, and there was talk of translating it into English and other languages. Why has it never been translated into English?

This was the question I found myself asking when I came across this short but extraordinarily rich and compact book, after a French friend had first introduced me to Ciaran Carson's book of translations of Follain poems, *From Elsewhere* (2014), a collection in which Follain accompanies Carson through some difficult historical territory. Selections of Follain's poetry have been translated into other languages but not his prose works about places, *Paris*, *Canisy* and *Chef-lieu*. The prose is a cousin of the poetry, more down-to-earth, more historically rooted, more humorous, but just as beautiful and surprising. We live in an ephemeral culture where a book is considered irrelevant and out of date after only a year or two. This is a pity because Follain's hybrid writing, and his apprehension of human history anticipate some of the preoccupations of our own time.

How do cities celebrate their heritage while adapting to change? Are cities for business and tourism or are they places for citizens to live, work and enjoy themselves, as Paris was in 1935? During Follain's lifetime the Fortifications were demolished, and the Zone was cleared away after 1956 to make way for the new Boulevard Periphérique, a four-lane ring road that was opened to cars in 1973. What would he have made of this replacement of the old hilly green belt by an asphalt barrier separating Paris from the suburbs outside? Some geographers and planners fear that Paris is becoming a museum city (*une ville musée*), while others promote the idea of the 15-minute city where inhabitants of all ages, incomes and professions can live and work comfortably and sustainably.

Paris has often been mythologised by writers, filmmakers and travellers, many of whom do not live there. Some recent versions show an unreal empty place filled with beautiful buildings but devoid of long-term inhabitants. Follain gives an alternative view, the perspective of someone from Normandy who has already spent ten years living and working there, someone who has an abiding awareness of past upheavals and long duration and a boundless curiosity about fellow citizens. His poetic portraits show Paris at a time of rapid and unregulated transformation, drawing in people from all the regions of France and from abroad, a place that is bustling and fascinating and alive.

Earth and Sky

One day I felt that there was earth under the paving stones of Paris, the old earth of landowners and land reformers; often the paving has become swollen from its force; on the eve of revolutions the paving stones are torn up, asphalt is broken, and the earth appears, poor earth it is true, but it strives to capture moisture from the sky.

If you wanted to walk for a long time towards the City, surrounded by all the sounds rising from the living hedgerows, you would see children playing under carts in the villages, hanging from the shafts, little ones settled by their mother inside the cart itself, village idiots so rooted to the same spot that they make sensitive souls weep because they remain dry-eyed when their father or mother dies. A glance would take in the car near the forge with its rustic driver sitting near sheafs of sparks. There would only be peace in the blue, or grey, or mauve eyes of voluptuous women cutting bread into decorated soup tureens.

Much later, you would make your way past big red villas, the setting for criminals and victims, and calm stately little girls measuring their height by garden sunlight. In these villas on dark oak shelves there are copies of *The Aeneid*, *The Iliad* and *The Odyssey* that the inhabitants no longer ever open. Finally, you would come across balding open spaces after some blossoming trees and a last labourer under a sooty sky.

There are places where the ground gives way. I know some people who harvest dandelions around a church near the Avenue de Clichy that they slowly boil down in big pots on gas stoves to reduce the bitter taste.

Meanwhile the stonemasons repairing the towers at Notre-Dame empty out pigeons' nests behind a cornice; the apprentice shouts with joy as he holds the chicks in his red hands while the head mason, smoking a clay pipe, has seen it all before. Around them fly the swallows and the bell-tower swifts but they are becoming rarer because fumes from the city are altering the purity of the sky, but the sky will win and so it's important to maintain that the birds will reappear and that the old woman with her stick and the beggar with his pouch will resist the dazzling, all too human, glass and stone constructions that impose their geometry on the earth; soft mosses will still flourish on dirty brushes left in the damp sink.

It's good to cross Paris as though it were a village. We will be moved at the thought of the last little cobbler when he has become acclimatised to the highest storey of a future skyscraper and puts on his spectacles to see the dying sun. On Sundays he'll take refuge in the Père-Lachaise cemetery near the Marshalls' tombs° [1] but when the little cobbler dies nobody will see his likes again, his memory will live on in one flower, one specific blade of grass, carefully filed in the dictionaries where it will be given its name.

All the girls crossing the Place de l'Opéra, the beautiful clever ones and the stupid ones with such beautiful eyes, know this eternal truth. The knowledge is in their blood

---

1. A degree sign (°) indicates that the expression is explained in the Translator's Notes at the end of the book.

and their flesh and mucous membranes destined for happy graves.

This is what Paris teaches us: they are here to last, the earth and sky.

The Sentiments

The allegorical map of the sentiments° always needs to be redrawn. The path taken by women and men down from the heights of La Courtille° has long been hacked away by pickaxes; but the skies are still the same, they contain the same subtle nuances; they are tinted with plumes of smoke that rise from everywhere, from the little café-restaurant as well as those rich apartments where dark wood 1880s furniture is coming back into vogue with the latest group of idle women who, because they cannot spend time in far-away lands, smoke Turkish cigarettes. As for the factory smoke, the sky absorbs that too, the old medieval blue sky that some dream-merchants have tried to scale, while writing some extremely beautiful love poems into the bargain. Around the Lycée Henri IV, and along the Quai de Bercy, the sky takes on the coloration of engravings and you can see sunrays coming up from under the clouds like the ones in holy pictures representing God the Father.

In certain bedrooms where people make love there is always someone waiting. When you go into others a musty smell catches your throat, so tragic when the woman living there takes off her shabby black clothes one by one. In another part of town, the man is to be found lying on a bed always at the same time of day, wearing his blue overalls with his hands crossed at the nape of his neck while the woman who wakes him does so in a sing-song voice; sounds from the street reach them along with the smell of damp leaves from a big park where nannies enjoy good health and a regular heartbeat. Sometimes they have mysterious marks on their skin, but their white stockings reinforce a strength of will worthy of opera.

Paris produces young lovers who have known only the chilly concrete of recently built apartments and never encountered a knot in a piece of timber, the rust of old residences or cracked dry paint on brown gates. After they have gassed themselves their orphaned cat miaows.

Women devoted to the sentiments, your 1880s sister wearing a golden helmet went up the stairs with a lover who had a large rose tattooed on his arm in two colours. She held the bottle of brandy and the decanter of cassis while the man carried a large plate of opened oysters on his big, outstretched palms.

Looking out from the window at suspicious groups of people loitering in the street, she twisted her hair firmly and expertly and the V-shapes that her arms made as she piled her chignon up high gave her concern a new grace.

Literature and life warm each other: a man takes to the laneways, his heart pounding, his body wrapped in a second-hand overcoat and with a cane in his hand he returns to his own place, from which he cannot banish the distinctive lingering heliotrope fragrance that girls leave behind; with red sleep-encrusted eyes he inspects the walls and finds near his shaving mirror a few drops of his own congealed blood, blood that he has never shed in riots or wars. He undresses and to take off his shirt lifts his arms high: specks of dust slowly settle in his underarm hair.

The bedroom is decorated with yellowing photographs: soldiers in epaulettes, prosperous men in silk hats seated in armchairs who look surprised, like Gouffé the bailiff° at that fatal hour when Gabrielle Bompart wound her dainty dressing-gown cord around his neck.

Old images come to his rescue now that he is sitting thinking on his bed where he has folded back the peony-coloured bedspread, images of Flanders or Artois, majolica ladies smiling at a miner repairing a Davy lamp, images of the South, of burning hot walls.

He doesn't forget that he has wedged copies of *Salammbô*, *Un prêtre marié*, the *Odelettes* and the *Poèmes saturnins* on the bookshelf but he starts to fret about a hole in a sock and a fading velvet collar and his books have become damaged with the pages yellowing around the edges; damp, dust and the atmosphere have all taken their toll; it's true that he still possesses some fine gold-edged volumes but his shoes are letting in the wet and on rainy days they are shapeless and dull; how much elbow grease he would need to get them back to a comforting shiny state!

He sleeps in old sheets that his mother embroidered; he has caught a chill. His window looks out on the Seine. In his feverish state his memories are like poisonous flowers, magnified, amplified and disturbing, as they merge into Marseilles or Rouen.

Solitude

The wanderer, walking among people with lowered heads going to their offices and businesses, and among delightful women, shivers with winter in his overcoat. When evening comes, he's drawn by the lights, his ear registers the first chords of music in the big cafés where business is not good, their owners smiling at the scarce customers; when he's jostled at the main intersections, he feels the sharp bite of the north-east wind.

He loves the warmth of home, even though he's escaping from it, he loves meat juices, magnificent silverware, he stops at shopfronts that display food and he studies the produce.

Sometimes you see him walking on the uneven footpath on the Quai de l'Oise: he watches little wrinkles form on the water, or else the row of brown front doors on the side where there are houses, he passes near the bar with flaking paintwork, with its sign in yellow letters that have forked tips and a shading effect that required a lot of work on the part of the handsome whistling painter in his bowler hat and white overalls.

When the aroma of grilling meat rises beside the horse-drawn caravan on the waste plot and the towers of the Trocadéro° stand out sharply against the bluish sky, the wanderer is brought back to the hot scent of the old days when the earth would crack, and waves of foam formed on the workhorses' collars.

In the gardens beside the Trocadéro a Sorbonne professor weighed down by the advancing years holds his head in his hands. One of the museums slumbers with its dugout canoes, its Aztec mummies, its arrows that were once poisoned; in the other museum plaster reproductions of cathedral doorways representing the Last Judgement stand out in their whiteness against the encroaching night. The stone hippopotamus, a sample of an architectural style in decline, seems astonishing to the infantry soldier with rough hands. A nurse holding a book, enchanted, follows the movements of the marvellous aquarium fish as they drift off to sleep.

You are the first to have the honour, said Brillat-Savarin to the master chef La Planche, of presenting an immense fried turbot to an amazed public. Brillat also mentions a dish fit for kings: spinach cooked in quail fat. At dusk in very peaceful streets the wanderer might imagine similar food; then there is immense exasperation with the evening; you can hear the silvery chimes of a private chapel; men pass by dressed in quality suits that, worn this day for the first time, still smell of the tailor's workshop, perfumed sad men who have childhood memories of snowy roads and sunlight. But then the quiet streets lead to sinister ones, the wanderer strolls along the high walls of a prison, and then a whole series of wide entrances with signage in black letters above them.

Soon he finds brighter districts; in little cafés men and women who have nothing in particular to do let themselves go.

In his own neighbourhood the wanderer has taken to greeting the shopkeeper as she washes in the morning. She's not one of those former stars that you sometimes encounter but a lost countrywoman who eats a dish made of bread soaked in city skimmed milk, near scrap metal relentlessly eroded by rust, near fragile moths that have hatched out in her flowery silks. A lot of old ladies like this lived during the time of frequent rioting, when impassioned and shy young men would eat alone in creameries, and suddenly turning pale in the lamplight, look nervously in their pockets for their single gold *louis d'or.*°

In the little streets where you can hear trains in the distance the heart of each household beats gently.

The person who has been wandering all day opens his window with a sinking feeling that things might not work out and his confidence begins to fade; he stares at a polished doorbell beside the entrance to a big apartment building across the street. It's the time of day when you might see shadows of students from the École Polytechnique sneaking over the wall, their smooth chins caught in the starlight.

It's good to breathe in the cool air. Those people who don't move on from Stendhal's cynicism have such musty ideas!

Monuments

The larger-than-life ornamental stone lions on either side of monumental entrances often go unnoticed. However, sometimes foreigners and people from the country do stop and look at them, as well as noticing the guardsmen sheltering in their sentry boxes.

Punctual people who are just as precise as their guidebooks get up early to visit historical monuments. There was a day when they left everything behind them in a provincial university town and lost contact forever with brown hair that was done up in a bun by nimble fingers reflected in the little gilded bedroom mirror above a grocery where the shopkeeper ground his Brazilian-blend coffee on the pavement.

They pass through those museums where every type of cough can be heard as well as the slow footsteps of distinguished ladies, the kind who will be killed off by political agitators when the time is ripe, the same ladies who walk in the Tuileries gardens carrying enormous flowers purchased in the Rue Saint-Honoré; their lips are sharply outlined in blood red while their faces become dreamy in front of Tintoretto's canvasses; their eyes focus on the greenish landscapes with paths that wind away in the distance behind the heads of eminent Italians. The museum regular whose face is deeply lined can also hear a group of young English girls laughing in a distant room. Sometimes he's tired and sits on a red velvet-covered sofa, staring trance-like at the shiny parquet floor; when he looked through the big landing window opening out over the courtyards, he noticed how black the sky was: soon the storm breaks with cloudbursts sweeping over Paris while amplified rumbles of thunder follow. Like Monsieur Bertin in the portrait by Ingres he has placed his hands on his knees; he sits there pensively in front of the stiff emperor leading the Retreat from Russia, painted by Meisonnier and titled *1814*.

He thinks of everything he has seen: the Eiffel Tower with all its illuminations; Cugnot's Steam Engine at the Conservatoire des Arts et Métiers that would move you to tears because it is made out of wood and indestructible iron: it's a well-known fact that it went out on the highways during the reign of Louis XVI where it polluted the countryside for the first time; the Victor Hugo museum where you can see an example of the uniform worn by members of the Académie Française and the one worn by the Peers of France, clothes that belong to an age when people did not baulk at doing elaborate embroidery; the tomb at Les Invalides and the old men who guard it, who are sometimes kind, sometimes impatient and touchy, and who have postprandial meetings on fine summer evenings around the cannons on the esplanade, gazing up at the sky like old shepherds watching the stars being formed. Finally, he saw the foetuses in yellow jars at the Anthropology Museum that were taken from a drowned woman from Morbihan who threw herself into the water on an enchanted evening near Châtelet wearing a flannelette blouse and a red petticoat; a clerk from the Hôtel de Ville involuntarily grimaced when he saw the body being brought up out of the water and afterwards when there was nothing left to see he went to his usual wine merchant and from this vantage point the whole architecture of Notre-Dame was visible with all its stone-carved fauna: the pelican, the elephant and the lark.

I remember an engraving in an illustrated paper that depicted an Englishman with yellow side-whiskers beating up a man on the Avenue de l'Opéra, while overlooking the scene was Apollo holding up his lyre. Nobody now throws ink at Carpeaux's sculpture° of the group of dancers, Carpeaux whose son wrote a book about Chinese torture methods. Sometimes the lorry containing stage sets stops at a side entrance of the monumental opera house; the stage set warehouse is located on a bleak outer boulevard, a big, red-bricked building ornamented with theatre masks. The concierge's office looks out on a little grassy courtyard where a donkey can be seen grazing.

Squares, Gardens, Parks, Arcades

The big parks were enclosed with pointed railings. The squares were surrounded only with low iron fences. Sometimes a bandstand has been erected in the middle.

People with worries take refuge in the squares to go over and over the muddled story of their lives; their fingers move feverishly as they try to repair the old overcoat of a dreamed-of destiny woven from mist and gold threads, never fulfilled. In the harsh sunlight trees spread their joyful foliage while children build sand fortifications.

Women knit, having placed coloured balls of wool on their knees. Every square has its own regulars. There are old Jewish men debating in the Square d'Anvers, in the Square de Batignolles misanthropic bachelors keep all their kindness for the birds that they feed with a few breadcrumbs while they take pleasure in the murmuring of the little man-made streams.

In autumn men sometimes mechanically gather dead leaves that they crush in their hands; some greedily breathe in a whiff of earth mould, others sit weakly on the benches, light-headed from hunger, and they think they can smell that odour of burnt hooves that rises beside cavalry barracks. For them this smell brings back an adolescent memory linked to hunger because long ago they used to pass by the farriers on their way home from night classes.

For many of the people who frequent squares the glacial

night in their hearts is rarely relieved by a warm breeze. There are middle-aged people ruminating, blind people serious in their shiny clothes to whom dwarf girls read under a grey sky, sickly boys lighting a cigarette while the old lady sitting near them wrinkles her nose. She wears a slightly yellowing crepe veil, and her face, once weather-beaten by gusts of salt wind outside her Breton house with its gorse and sharp grass, is hard and sad.

When night starts to fall the children, who have done a lot of shouting, fall asleep. Marvellous mothers stroke them gently and their voices rising from warm bodies grow fainter in the twilight. They seem sophisticated in their slightly faded satin or slightly dull velvet clothes. The red autumn leaves fall on their shoulders; they push their prams towards the exit, their children sleeping in the lace, and for many of them who have a love song running through their heads, the crunch of gravel under their feet, the squeak of the low iron gates that you have to hinge open, are like an orchestra playing the gentle melancholy of the city.

In the Palais Royal gardens, you understand how magnificent secrets can be captured in stone. In the golden midday dust blond children stopping their big hoops under the fading leaves are surprised by the little cannon. But the faint smell of dust doesn't mingle the way it used to with the appetising aromas wafting from the famous kitchens of former times. Nevertheless, rotisserie vapours have given a patina to the old mortar; at Véfour, the last refuge of chess-players, the sound of bourgeois celebrations is no more, but the restaurant is still there. Carefully poking his head out of his hole, a rat watches the *blanquette à l'ancienne* being prepared, while in the little bedroom overlooking the gardens, above a lace shop, a lover organises ladybird races on his mistress's dainty breast.

The wedding parties in the restaurant at the Buttes Chaumont enjoy their permission to stroll among the rockeries and green spaces all night long under the stars; the patent leather shoes worn by abattoir workers crunch on the gravelled walks bordered by sandy beds deposited there by heavy rains; minuscule skin fragments from milky-skinned red-haired women float among the leaves; common-or-garden aquatic birds sleep on the cool lawn. The black bridge looms up and from here people often take their lives, wearing sad jackets woven at Roubaix.

On the Fourteenth of July, and on this day alone, the denizens of the Buttes-Chaumont are allowed to walk, sit or lie on the grass. This is why you can see, at the corner of a mound near a wine stain sinking into the earth, the spot where a woman's back lay stretched as she slept in the blue afternoon.

When the day ends, the fireworks dazzle and blaze and afterwards young people set light to newspapers and wrapping paper. Policemen have fun rolling down the slopes, hidden in the complicit darkness.

In the Parc Montsouris the middle classes are more restrained. Here the smell of cut hay mingles with fumes from the Sceaux railway line while a red-eyed old maid sleeps right beside the monument commemorating the expedition led by Flatters in the Sahara.°

★

Thousands of years hence will it be possible for a school-child to confuse the Place de la Concorde° with the Hanging Gardens of Babylon? The central obelisk that ornaments it weighs two hundred and fifty thousand kilos; some evenings the Ministry of the Marine on one side and the Palais-Bourbon on the other are shrouded by the kind of steamy mists that rise from man-made lakes in the countryside coated with royal green.

The sculptor has painstakingly worked the folds on the tunics worn by the heavy-set women representing the cities of France. The name and layout of the Place de la Concorde belong to that time when the map of French African colonies in the pastel-coloured atlas was decorated with an engraving depicting a naked, brown-skinned child sitting on an Arab's lap. This child was kissing a little white child who sat on the lap of a robed woman holding a tablet inscribed with the words Justice and Fraternity.

As for the former Place Royale with its beautiful pink houses, it has become the Place des Vosges. It was here in the Place Royale that a lady on a bench explained to her neighbour: 'I know my history, you see, they came by over there with the head of one of the Duchesses of Lamballe on a pike, they had gone to find the Dauphin and they killed him; but what on earth do you expect, the kings were starving the people!'

During working hours, the men they say don't do a tap of work all day long meet up in the covered passages. They are dressed in those old light-coloured coats that race-goers wear and have stomach-churning memories of sunsets at the Auteuil racecourse.

In the arcades the slightest cough is amplified; you hear stooped people spitting nearby, walking with their hands in their pockets and spikes of hair sticking out from under felt hats.

The arcades are the place to go if you want to study the black-aproned watchmaker, the symbol of hardworking civilisation. He disassembles the clockwork in all those watches that mark the hour on people's hearts on days when there are meetings, festivals and inaugurations and on evenings when lovers stroll. The Paris watchmaker eats soup and drinks wine and often has a calm straightforward demeanour; at local wedding parties girls admire his white hands softened by the gleam of blue steel. Oh bare-skinned women on summer days stretching out your delicate arms towards platinum timepieces on bedside tables, how graceful your image appears to the man who falls asleep facing the *grisaille* landscape wallpaper in his bedroom while Westminster chimes sound!

Churches

Notre-Dame changes colour every day. The cathedral is still a great church for the seasons. In December you can wander there in the cold silence looking at the purples, prune-coloured violets and oxide blues in the frozen stained glass.

Notre-Dame parish is poor. On important days in the ecclesiastical calendar, it has been known for a priest married in a registry office to slip into the processions in his surplice, recognised by his pale astonished child who is hushed up by the mother.

Notre-Dame is where the graceful daughters of the Chief of Police get married. It was in the shadow of its towers that Javert,° the mythical policeman, left his silky top hat on the bank and let himself fall into the sparkling water.

In Saint-Sulpice every Sunday the caped seminarians sing at the lectern – two, four or six of them depending in the importance of the feast day. Old sacristans dip their fingers into giant conch shells, a gift from Louis XIV. Delacroix's painting, *The Expulsion of Heliodorus*, lights up a gloomy side chapel; it was an object of contemplation for sensitive intellectuals at the end of the nineteenth century, men who used to wear sharply pointed shoes that scraped on the flagstones.

Saint-Germain-des-Prés is flanked by its charmingly worldly presbytery. The magnificent original capitals survive inside this church, but the frescos painted by Flandrin are losing their significance. They are no longer actively admired even though they were greeted by sumptuous organ pieces when they were first unveiled during the Second Empire.

In Paris the decline of the churches is conducive to reflection, churches with beautiful apses overlooking devastated squares: at Saint-Séverin, above a little side doorway, Saint Martin is depicted cutting the actual heavy fabric coat which, according to the legend about him, reflected all the colours of sunset along the old road. In the Rue de la Huchette, with its narrow frontage and distinctive smells, almost opposite Saint Martin's doorway, you can see a dairy painted sky-blue with its sign: *At the Holy Child*. Set back from the windswept Place du Panthéon, Saint-Étienne-du-Mont is still there like an intact jewel. It was in this church, with his mitre on his head and his crook in his hand, that Bishop Sibour was assassinated one feast day by a priest who had been suspended and who let out a mysterious shout while stabbing the bishop in the heart: 'No goddesses.'

In Saint-Eustache when special masses are held for the people working in the markets, the girls from the tripe and cheese stalls, wearing their white aprons and cream-coloured shawls wrapped around their bosoms, take turns to attend a bit of the ceremony. Near Colbert's tomb that was sculpted by Coysevox they listen to a sermon about Lazarus being brought back to life and the sound of their clogs rings out clearly.

Notre-Dame-des-Victoires has associations with pious wasp-waisted officers back from the Crimea and Italy, the same officers who took part in the Corpus Christi procession while they recovered from their injuries, holding the canopy ropes in the courtyard of the Val-de-Grâce hospital alongside army children swinging the censors.

Sometimes beneath the starry blue porch ceilings at Saint-Germain-l'Auxerrois, when the congregation shivers under stout umbrellas in the stinging March rain, you can hear a funeral tribute for a successful haberdashery merchant. His plump daughters wear veils and are curvaceous but graceful while their cousins in half mourning appear delicate and washed out.

In the brightest Parisian light, the frieze on the Madeleine depicts the Last Judgement.

One afternoon in Saint-Honoré-d'Eylau on All Saints' Day I saw the pulpit with its well-polished wood. A corpulent priest was speaking; the light falling on him caught the pink silk underneath the lace sleeves of his alb. He was comparing the soul in purgatory to an imperfectly cut diamond. He grew animated, citing famous words and worthy deaths. I could see his strong earthly hands gripping the edge of the chiselled pulpit.

There is still often something poignant about Paris churches. I'm thinking of those posters for pilgrimages that catch in a gust of wind when you open the felt-lined doors, those abandoned lecterns, the servant woman reciting *Hail Marys* in front of big, blackened paintings set in Jesuit architecture, and the worker cursing as he shifts the burden on his shoulders on a dark noon at the end of a big funeral when lightning flashes in the sky.

Hospitals and Prisons

The Parisian face of sickness and death is shrouded in the romantic aura of illustrations, like the one depicting the cape worn by bibulous hearse drivers, or the one that shows the Jardin des Feuillantines, or, closer to our time, the picture of the jolly major from the Great War.

Women selling flowers and bearded purveyors of stale goods cluster around the entrances to military and civilian hospitals. Girls from the lower classes, young shop assistants or lovesick dressmakers, often speak plainly and simply about chest infections, tumours and cancers. Nurses with bright eyes and well-kept hands come with the smile of destiny bearing, as a special favour, pureed peas and chicken legs. Scenes of epidemics, peace and war unfold slowly inside their heads.

One day I happened to be in the hospital visiting Ferdinand, a police officer who was wasting away with an unmentionable disease, a tall fellow with a decadent emperor's face and a friendly expression whose mother was a grocer in a little Norman town. I found him covered in swellings but still able to appreciate the branches that you could glimpse from the windows.

Ferdinand spoke about the time when he was just a town sergeant, still in his *soutane*, as he put it when describing his uniform, on traffic duty at the Palais Royal; one day he was stopped by a wrinkled dwarf wearing white gaiters, yellow gloves and a colourful bowler hat. The midget asked: 'Excuse me officer, could you direct me to a public edifice?' Then Ferdinand, who is built like a colossus, leaned down to the little man and answered in a broad accent, 'A public edifice, would that be to drop a log or to have a piss?'

Ferdinand's girlfriend liked to dress in light fabrics and was extremely fastidious and came to see him every day. Ferdinand got better; he continued working in Vice,° a job for which, he said, he had nothing but contempt; he was to be seen again walking at sunset with his hat over one ear, his hands behind his back, along the pathways in the Bois de Boulogne. On the rue de Rivoli the girls liked him, he gently convinced them to take turns in Saint-Lazare and would shake his head in indignation when he told you stories about this women's prison, once a leper house. It's still a sinister place with a grubby tricolour flag hanging above the entrance, wardens warming themselves around an old-fashioned stove and the odd young inmate passing by inside carrying some linen in a knotted handkerchief.

The girls leaving Saint-Lazare walk back quickly to the commercial districts that are full of ribbons, cafés and nourishment. The young men, when they leave La Santé, if they don't walk at the brisk pace of a country postman, linger at the bar called *La Bonne Santé* just opposite the prison where they discover complicit coolness and warmth again.

Department Stores

The store detective in his brown jacket is leaning on the banisters at the main staircase; for two hours now, he has been keeping an eye on the shoplifter with her ringed fingers rummaging feverishly in the linen so that he can have her stopped at the exit.

The hands move slowly on the clocks, women in mourning stop by at crucifixes; already the shoplifter feels the forceful policemen's grip, big fellows with strong-smelling breath under the coloured lighting.

Meanwhile the sales assistants test the sound of crystal that has come out of the furnace. At the detachable-collar counter, pretty girls demonstrate the different styles with a professional disinterest as their hearts beat under their black dresses. At times a fleeting worry flickers in their glazed eyes. Their skin is white, sometimes golden, even ochre-toned. The lift chimes. All the customers are treated with respect, even those prematurely aged young women with a hump or a lopsided walk who come to purchase lace and ribbons to adorn themselves.

Cemeteries

At Charonne cemetery, on a mound covered with wild vegetation and enclosed by badly rusted railings (railings that have seven or eight different designs thanks to the devotion of the artisans who made them), there stands in his Ancien Régime suit, wearing a tri-cornered hat and tails, the statue of Bègue, also known as Magloire. An inscription on the plinth lists his occupations and qualities and the positions he held: a painter by trade, historian, *philosophe* and secretary to M. de Robespierre. A reminder of the great Revolution that came into being when cautious politics failed because of grain prices.

The little Charonne graveyard, with its wrought-iron crosses, children's tombs, mossy urns and baroque epitaphs inside ivy-eroded vaults, deserves this fine cloudless blue sky that delights the urban and suburban drivers and delivery men employed by the Bazar de l'Hôtel de Ville.

One of the epitaphs says of the deceased: *He was not able to reap the reward of his profits and savings …* It's a fine example of a redundant expression. The dead man's silk hat must have been decorated with a sumptuous purple label bearing the hat-maker's name in gold letters.

The Père-Lachaise cemetery, the final stronghold of the Communards,° still retains smells from the last century when several suburban villages merged with Paris. M.

Thiers, a dwarf with a fine intellect whose glorious image can still be seen in old houses all over the countryside, is buried there in an immense square mausoleum. Some of the tombs belonging to Napoleon's generals are still tended, many are not. Here the man in search of an emotional experience, with dandruff on his lapels, discovers old muddy wreaths and with his spatulate fingertips traces carvings of eagles on mossy stone.

During the fine season when vegetation grows abundantly and poppies and wild oats sway in uncleared corners the sheer number of memorial columns, amphoras and crosses makes your heart beat faster: this is how things are not far from the wall where blood was spilled.

Around the crematorium the columbarium is a great library of urns. Sceptical lower middle-class people, who viewed the world stubbornly and gently when they were alive, choose to be incinerated here, along with moderate principled workers. If their ashes are ranged high along the wall, their relatives have to use a ladder to pay their respects and climb up to the numbered niche located among so many others.

You can visit the crematorium furnace. The architecture in the cremation room is reminiscent of Solomon's temple. There is an organ. The coffin passes through an imitation oven decorated with stucco roses and then removed and slid down a passage past only two relatives into the real oven that consumes just about everything, for in the cinders only some fragments of bone are to be found.

During the public opening hours, the oven is on standby. I noticed among some women visitors a lower middle-class lady dressed in black, and her face was lit by the pink glow as she called out laughing: 'Well *I'd* be comfortable here, seeing as I like the heat!'

But the widows who believe in the resurrection of the body have had monstrous tombs built in Père-Lachaise cemetery for their late husbands; one tomb is an enormous tower that climbs like a factory chimney towards the sky; another is ornamented by gigantic symbolic women with closed eyes.

Sometimes, sitting on a bench beside a path, two old men who were in business together talk loudly about how porous the ground is as they plan their future graves. They imagine the damage that might occur near their bodies due to underground water filtering in, while the birds seek out Francis of Assisi in a last ray of sunlight.

The Botanical Gardens

In the Jardin des Plantes homesick army men go to lean over the bear pit. These gardens are a symbol of idleness, curious wandering, and the sad gentle world of encyclopedias.

Around five o'clock in the evening, the sharp autumn breeze shakes the labels with their Latin names among the clumps of trees and blows strongly enough to make the obsessive type feel a shudder of anxiety, the man whose mind is growing muddled, whose memory is going and who in the golden light of an oil lamp once dreamed of knowing everything.

The bears provide an image of peaceful animal existence on fine evenings that lend themselves to philosophical discussion; exiled country folk cannot see any resemblance between the little birds they are familiar with and the solemn tufted or crested creatures here with their brightly patterned red and green plumage.

In the museum visitors look at wax models while lorry-drivers' shouts can be heard in the distance. Butterflies' wings stuck on pins produce a barely perceptible dust. As chance would have it there might be a young woman hiding near the diplodocus, trembling for fear that she will be found by her pimp who is looking for her in the quiet little streets nearby.

In the ashy heat haze that you get in these fine gardens

when a torrid summer has baked everything dry except for some hardy green rockery plants, I know some people who once felt something unutterable, an otherworldly, delicious twinge of nostalgia as they drank cool clear water from a cup on a chain and ate one of those bread rolls meant for feeding the animals.

In what was formerly the King's Garden, old servant women who have been fired go to cry on the benches while the gardener and his assistants quietly rake the gravel.

An author who was once a police inspector tells how the young pimps used to kill the wood pigeons in the gardens with slings and then put out their eyes; they wanted women to fear and admire them.

In this earthly paradise, with its cedar plateau, glasshouses, orangeries and rough earth patches, the men of the Republic strolled in their black frock coats; their children weren't very far away, watched by nannies from the country, women of few words knitting garments out of white wool.

At night-time the animals' cries, even when they sometimes grow insistent, barely disturb the caretaker's blissful daughter as she sleeps.

The Law Courts

Many unfortunates come to warm themselves here; you can also see old flatterers. In the great entrance hall, there is the monument to Berryer° and the one to Tronchet in bas-relief that shows Louis XVI's three lawyers visiting the monarch; he is seated near a globe while behind him the loyal Cléry weeps.

In appearance, judges can be vulgar or noble or sad and some seem jolly while others are naturally serious or pretend to be and they all carefully weigh up circumstantial detail and contingencies: the law continues to be a great Roman creation, exhaustively examining cases of violence and corruption. Napoleon, between two battles, got to grips with its workings and structure. Jurisprudence still draws on this fine doctrine, and there is something comforting in the sight of an eminent jurist built like a colossus, such as one of the current members of the Supreme Court. This man was previously the Dean of a law faculty that he ran supremely well, and on gentle evenings when mist rose from the meadows, he inspired affection for his giant form which could often be seen on the wide avenue of an old Norman town.

Of course, there are many among the more noteworthy members of the Bar who understand nothing of humanity. Others receive their clients in offices that are run on principles of byzantine complexity! Still, there are others who remain true.

In the galleries people give free rein to their fondness for empty conversation, whereas in the sessions sometimes the judges, prosecutors and defence can too easily run to joking while a tribunal is whispering its judgement, while in the dark, richly decorated gallery of the Appeal Court the medieval pointed shoes slowly wear down on a hideous life-size statue of Saint Louis standing under a little oak tree.

In popular parlance the Palais de Justice is known as 'the Great Palace'. Travelling along its corridors, venturing into the audience chambers, up flights of stairs, along the ceilings and glasswork, the observant eye can make out innumerable allegorical representations: lictors' fasces, hands of justice, scales, Gaulish cockerels, laurel and oak wreaths. In a far-off future, in strong summer sunlight, people will carefully dig up all these emblems and write commentaries on them.

Theatres and Cinemas

At the entrance to the Théâtre-Français people wait for hours to get the cheap seats that are not sold in advance, so that they can see the noble tragedies. A pale young man leans on the smooth upright of a column, ladies not endowed with good looks do their crochet (they are far removed from Von Arnim's° beautiful heroine who with one intense gaze could empty out the contents of a pomegranate); they only consider the subsidised plays worthy of attention, for them breastplates, togas, daggers and poisons belong to the realm of poetry. Many moons ago these ladies who waited used to accept their seats in the galleries at previews not without quibbling with their neighbours while Paul Mounet° was still at his table in the Café de la Régence; the stage hand, following orders, told him for the fourth time that his name was on the poster for that evening and that he had to hurry up to be on stage in time; he grumbled in reply: 'Yes, yes, you little shit, I'm coming, I'm coming.' But he would leave things to the very last minute. He was a good man who always chatted to the roadmenders as they dug in the yellow trenches, repairing the streets.

Going through an inner courtyard with gutters and a pediment where the corridors of a popular playhouse open out, you can hear an actress laughing, surrounded by flowers, young men, and puppies. On cold days especially, you think of people setting off to war, of the endless stream of excited young recruits for whom the theatre girls are the epitome of culture.

The house beside the road with fox traps around the garden, of course it felt like peace then.

The old-school worker used to joyfully climb the steps of the Ambigu° to see melodramas that were as satisfying as a loaf of bread and a bottle of wine; hearing the coachman crack his whip on the Lyon stagecoach or the bells of Saint-Sulpice ring out in *The Beggarwoman* gave him a zest for life.

One evening an old workman was sitting in the upper gallery of the Ambigu; the play that evening was *La Porteuse de Pain*. At the interval after the first act, he started telling a fat lady sitting beside him what was going to happen next: much later the heroine's son would find a letter torn into tiny little pieces, the letter that would exonerate his mother; the child had fed the letter to his cardboard horse as make-believe oats. The old man explained: 'So you see, they discovered her innocence through the horse's arse.' Although he was seeing the play for the twentieth time he felt 'stirred' and even this time he was in tears, then he looked at the chandelier, spoke about how heavy it was and compared it to the one in the Grand Opera that Gaston Leroux° imagines falling on the heads of all the fine ladies and gentlemen present.

At the neighbourhood concert on Saturdays, housewives mind their men's hats on their laps. All day their knees bent for scrubbing were weary, as were their smiles to their neighbours, amidst the softest of greys and subtlest of purples; their hair shone brightly among all the colourful aperitifs.

On one such evening they watch the double-muscled Rigoulot, the strongest man in the world. His young wife on the stage explains all the records he has broken while her colossal husband remains silent and demonstrates his skills with gentle eyes.

The sight of such strength, combined with such an absence of malice, makes all the hard men in the audience feel strangely uneasy as they roll their cigarettes and nod their heads in the shadows.

At a matinee in one of the big cinemas the occasional film-goer settles down cosily in his seat to enjoy as much comfort as possible. The icy politeness of the usherettes in their rustling silks, the people around him dressed in solid British wool, the landscapes on the screen, the soundtrack of murmuring streams and tumbling waterfalls, all conjure up a sophisticated melancholy that he savours in a gentle torpor.

At the same time in a little cinema on the Avenue de Saint-Ouen, eager children from the poor area nearby° can gaze at hackneyed images of old silent films for fifteen sous. Their bright shining eyes follow the flint-jawed detective as with one dextrous movement he breaks open the false cigar containing smuggled cocaine.

At four in the morning in the suburban cinemas the soul devoted to beautiful screen heroines with flawless skin breathes a last sigh as the smell of oranges grows fainter.

Maybe the poor film-star, whose body is gradually falling apart, sick and tired of jealous fits and brief flings, disgusted with flowers and gold vanity cases, is at this moment opening her window and looking out at the first rays of dawn coming up over the Champs-Élysées.

Montmartre

At the Sacré-Cœur basilica, built by special act of parliament, the observer grows emotional when a dog howls pitifully at the foot of the monumental steps on squally evenings. Not long ago, wild radish grew out of the earth in the garden belonging to the station master who ran the old funicular. When the transport system was streamlined, the old funicular disappeared leaving a lingering wisp of steam along the steep slope. At the top of the Sacré-Cœur on easy evenings, Delobelle,° Rastignac and the 1912 poets° come to mind while literature, that familiar inner sun, helps you digest meat dishes and wine and you are draped in a soft warm overcoat.

I remember a small town from my childhood, going into a gloomy tent where there was an acrobat with blue eyelids dancing in a sequinned dress. The garlicky smell of acetylene lamps mingled with the strong scent of pine trees wafting from the cemetery, the tent canvas did not close properly and there were gaping openings showing the night sky. A poor devil in a tight-fitting jacket sang:

It's midnight and Montmartre lights appear . . .°

There is a treacherous illusory way of life that seems supremely emancipated to those living it, on the margins as the sentimental song has it, while they listen to the echoes of bourgeois carousing, and sit around their studio stoves smoking their pipes remembering harvest songs, it's a life-style that ends with the terribly human picture of Gaston Couté's° father by his son's graveside cursing 'the people who killed him', refusing to shake hands with pale or red-nosed bohemians and a few literary men in opera hats.

Under skies that are just as fine today, confused old men chew over the fodder of exquisite, gentle, troubling memo-ries: the triple and quadruple layers of frothy lace on wom-en's bloomers, rebellious young women who died from lacing their cream or pink corsets too tight, who lived a hand-to-mouth existence but who always insisted that the barman deliver them a Christmas tree drawn by a white horse. Fresh gilding in the cafés and steamy roses per-versely tucked into black stockings fuelled the artistic and literary dreams of a thousand and one nights whose fragile secrets are now lost.

Montmartre still has its ninety-year-old ladies, former artists' models, decked out like trinkets; these women, along with the angel-featured, tired housewives and chil-dren wearing hoods in the twilight, still lend Montmar-tre an air of slightly false refinement. Near the Rue Lepic, where there is a very good fish and meat market, little women bustle around uttering childish curses when they step on a broken paving stone or when the thin ice cracks under their slender shoes in wintertime. They often live in hovels decorated with flowers and are devoted to hygiene and scrubbing everything clean. They go to collect their milk in big chipped patterned jugs; sometimes they don't have time to put on a shirt and hide naked in a big fur coat that they pull tightly around themselves, pursing their heart-shaped lips.

The red-light district at Fort-Monjol has been demolished but the Boulevard de la Villette is still the same with its faded shops and cheap cafés full of emaciated North African gentlemen.°

On the Rue de Belleville, at a shop where a woman sells funeral wreaths, the window display has a little bicycle made of pearls, specially commissioned by the proud family of a racing cyclist in memory of the champion. An intangible cloud of flour from the bakery next door floats around the little funerary bicycle.

The last one-man band plays in a bistro where the boss remembers *louis d'or* coins and the smell of violet soap makes a young worker flare her fine nostrils.

On the Rue des Cascades in the café garden below street level cheerful customers in shirtsleeves are playing *boules.*

On the Rue des Envierges in a dimly lit dusty shopfront a globe is displayed along with a gold-lettered stick of India ink and letter cards bordered with a fine red line.

Girls with small ears, vast sad cinemas, and the little grey houses on the Allée des Soupirs give Belleville-Ménilmontant its glorious, gloomy, gentle aura of refinement.

There's something medieval about the markets district at first light. Butchers and flour merchants rub shoulders in the cafés; you only see healthy teeth and strong arms here. Gleaming spoons and hands gently wrapped around chunky glasses epitomise the old world of hard work, an image that Paris maintains since it stubbornly clings on to everything.

On their wedding morning, while they're having their hair curled, some sales agents' daughters are perhaps smiling at a private vision of a globe covered in flowers, dotted with animals and men and women dressed in dazzling costumes, resting under oaks, baobabs or cedars. The girls' white high-arched shoes gleam in the half-light while the mingled sounds of business transactions rise up from below.

On mass days for the market people who have died during the year, in his sermon about Lazarus coming back to life, the priest tries to reanimate the image of Jesus in the minds of the attractive red-haired girls who sell charcuterie and the handsome dark-eyed lads from the tripe stalls. After the ceremony, strong men with baskets and big white felt hats go to the sacristy to greet the archbishop of Paris, forever the enigmatic old man, for whom pious biographers lie in wait, tensing their restless, black-gloved hands.

One way to lighten the burden of care is to stride across the districts of Passy and Auteuil in the summer light around Saint Martin's Day! Strolling around Ranelagh you see bare ground where the short grass has been trodden down by children's nannies. The grandeur of old building materials, venerable stucco rendering, and grotesque masks asserts itself in the soft light and the houses built of purplish brick are home to professors who every morning shave with shaking hands.

For the men and women wandering through Auteuil or Passy, the noble name of mortal seems more appropriate than for passers-by elsewhere.

In the afternoons, speakers with faint voices give talks in buildings hidden behind curtains of trees. There is not much meeting of minds; the anecdote dries on the lips, but the widowed speaker's mouth freshened with liquorice no longer has that sickly morning breath that it did when he grimaced to adjust the button on his detachable collar.

Armfuls of flowers open their buds in bedrooms belonging to young women who are covered with kisses all day long, not kisses of love. Sometimes a rider with a rose between her lips gallops by on her piebald horse on the Avenue Henri-Martin; other young women serve curious customers in small bookshops. In the evening, out on the calm café terraces, there is a sense of peace when you touch a curved table's edge or a flared glass that contains a harmful but traditional drink; a woman in red passes by with jet-black hair.

Family-run guest houses have closed their shutters; on the Rue de la Source the Benedictines are beginning their compline. This peacefulness might be disturbed by a smell of dust falling on the flower beds. In the guest houses the wine is not strong and the table is set with several carafes of clear water.

The tall, grey houses visible from the Quai de Bercy° look like the ones you see in eighteenth-century prints. Bare-chested men are working on the riverbanks and heat exchange takes place while a liquid silence fills the barrels. At the Bal Nègre° in the Rocher de Cancale a big white-faced fellow has some African features. He's from America where he was able to have his hair straightened by a process invented over there by an old black woman who made a fortune out of it; sometimes he sneaks a look at the only remaining visible sign of his origins: the purple half-moons on his nails.

A fine dust has settled on the old-fashioned hand-chiselled streetlamps that ornament the parapet on the big bridge, the same dust that gets into the women's hair and the beads of sweat on their necks, dust and sweat forming a light film of dirt on their skin.

In dark oxblood bars, workmen covered in coaldust add wine to their bloodstreams. You can hear the metallic squeaking of cartwheels and their precise, elementary, complicated geometry tames the landscape, adding reflections to the silky waters.

The revolutions that swept in from the Faubourg Saint-Antoine have left a whiff of gunpowder on the Place de la Bastille at the spot where carpenters' planes smooth down oak wood and the lower middle-class man at the bistro chats to the muscular waiter.

At the terrace of the Canon de la Bastille, near the foot of the column, you can see white-haired shopkeepers, travelling salesmen who carry pocketfuls of samples, and middle-class men wearing faded Légion d'Honneur ribbons, all of them sipping their aperitifs.

The young person who has strayed among these people feels that intoxicating freshness that cities have when you encounter them for the first time, in pursuit of conquests and happiness.

*

At noon beneath the peristyle of the Bourse brokers perched on a balustrade shout and roar; they have tucked back their legs to grip the rails with their heels so that every surface of their shoes is visible: the uppers are shining, the soles are dirty with Paris mud and the heels are sometimes slightly worn down.

The Bourse is modelled on a temple dedicated to Vespasian, the emperor who had a large square head, who led a moderate life and wished to die standing upright. It is surrounded by statues of Industry, Agriculture, Commerce and Justice, draped female figures who sometimes stimulate ambition and pride in their frenzied followers.

However, real women made of flesh, with beautiful hips and eyes the colour of haymaking, interrupt the stockbrokers' lunches to find their husbands who the evening before, or the evening before that, slept near cars at a picnic while they gracefully dipped their dainty feet in a babbling woodland stream. Will they run away some day leaving behind a pale sunray on some lingerie abandoned over the back of a chair?

They walk around Paris without ever really noticing its monuments, yet on an exceptionally mild evening one of them once drew her companion's attention to the Sainte-Chapelle's spire against a fading rose-coloured sky.

Meanwhile bank tellers stand behind the counters and during a lull rearrange their hair with cupped hands; they escape in the evenings via the Rue Rambuteau, the Rue Réaumur and the Rue Vivienne. At the café terraces old men gaze at them, sitting behind glasses of clear water untouched by any cordial.

*

Sébastopol is a prestigious name. The Crimean war, if it must be mentioned, seems very far away, its bivouacs, the sisters of Charity with their rosary beads, and the corseted officers. Yet I do know a man who is thirty-four whose father was at the time a young camp follower of sixteen who went on the campaign of 1857. In 1913 he brought his son to see the Musée des Invalides; his son, who grew up fast, was born when his father was over sixty.

The Sébasto is nowadays an important boulevard containing traditional shops catering for solid families who are consumed by secrets and who respect the change of seasons, alongside spacious bars with old gilding, coloured lights and a shady clientele.

In the Hygiene Museum you can study various models of domestic latrines, designs for imperial and royal wagons, illustrations showing cross-sections of sewers (where the painter has carefully and in minute detail also shown the surface, that is, the street in 1880 with hansom cabs and soldiers with yellow collars). In the museum's roof space there are wax model displays of rotten meat and the lungs of tubercular animals. If you visit these collections on a Sunday, your ears are filled with the evening Magnificat from the Église Saint-Louis right next door.

The old Sébasto pimp prowls in front of the civil and military outfitters that are cheek by jowl with streets containing places of ill repute like the Bar des Japonaises, the Bar des Hirondelles and that Brasserie Franco-Belge where an old Spanish woman sitting between two beauties groans and laughs. The oldest profession still carries on, with manufactured affection as part of the carefully contrived plot, while simian heads calculate and white hands ply their trade.

The Latin Quarter

In the last century a procession of cabs was to be seen going from the Boulevard Saint-Michel to the Grands Boulevards, packed with students and young women, and on the roof of one of the cabs a shapely courtesan who had agreed to sit completely naked. The pavement was thronged with young people from the provinces mopping rustic sweat from their brows; their frock coats were white at the elbows. In a gilded café, a big chap with a blond beard held a seashell (picked up on one of those French beaches increasingly frequented by minor civil servants and prosperous shopkeepers) to the beautifully shaped ear of his mistress dressed in mousseline who was as thick as a plank: he wanted her to hear the sea.

You find all these still vivid images disconcerting because they need to be concentrated to release their unusual properties: young bucks ordering bitters, sprawling on the gothic chairs of the Taverne du Panthéon with their thumbs tucked into their waistcoats, chubby waitresses unaffected by the anaemia that was so prevalent then, professors chewing on pink radishes while expounding materialist doctrines.

Already during the same period, young priests, basking in the balmy May evening scents, were exchanging their buckled shoes for laced military boots and debating beneath the dome at the Sorbonne, that place so dear to Péguy who went on to die in the 'just war'.

In the Luxembourg gardens birds settle on the bronze horses' heads at Carpeaux's fountain. The wanderer becomes emotional when he sees the birds on a stormy afternoon because he wants to escape the strange apprehensiveness that's bothering him whereas the birds discover old familiar waters.

Foreigners enjoy walking through these gardens where so many gentle voices mingle. García Moreno, who was fervently devoted to the Virgin Mary, used to walk here with his friends before he became President of Ecuador.

A fierce summer sun slowly fades the bodices of cheap dresses worn by the seamstresses and fashionable women sitting on iron chairs not far from the statue of Verlaine. Near the flowerbeds the old men's dark clothes turn to red or else to green.

In 1925 a lot of little bars on the Boulevard Saint-Michel were shockingly poor. You could smell a residue of boiled milk and croissant flakes. From behind the café windows people watched out for the passers-by. It was the year of suicides and thefts. The man they called the boxer, who described himself as a worker in gold leaf, was nothing more than a thief who stole pedigree dogs from taxis. One day he was arrested near the Carrefour Jacob, while his friends were preparing buckwheat porridge in a garret; at a neighbouring business a young girl whose clothes had been stolen at an art students' ball and who had to go home entirely naked under an overcoat, was crying and asking for someone to go to find her a dress at her aunt's house at Grenelle. Later she gave birth to a child that she wanted to feed herself and who died after several weeks. One evening she was seen drunk on the arms of two students on the Rue Saint-Jacques, dressed in mourning clothes and shouting: she had taken out her engorged breasts from the top of her dress; on a street corner hungry people were conversing in lowered voices beside big white posters with black letters.

At the Grand Comptoir de la Maubert the manager rolls his dazzling white shirtsleeves up to his elbows. This is where the market for sorted and unsorted half-smoked cigarettes takes place; it's also where they offer you, as an unexpected find, a pair of Belgian or Spanish army boots. In order to pay, an old man takes out, one after the other, old coins bearing the head of Napoleon III.

Not many young people in the university district are interested in knowing that a certain professor, a humble man but a great theologian, has just died in Ethiopia where he was sent on a mission to the court of the Negus. However, two of his grieving friends do talk about him in a small bar where they have come to break bread together and one of them drinks warmed water while the other drinks rough wine. The stove goes out, they are almost alone and can remember him better that way.

However, in the square under the faded sky at Saint-Germain-des-Prés a young woman rests her head on an old student's strong shoulder, a draper or a labourer's son. Briefly, in a micro-realisation that also takes in the church and the foliage, you sense the connection between the scholastic theologian, a man who had many children, and the carefree couple. Sometimes, exactly as the young man and woman are doing now and in this same neighbourhood, the professor used to follow a swallow's flight.

The Left Bank

In a café on the Boulevard du Montparnasse, government ministers who have just resigned meet up to spend the rest of the night together. Bored or drunk women pass by, indifferent to their eloquence.

At midday in bright bedrooms joyful foreign women are lustily having showers, a diamond sparkles on a shelf; a red-headed woman, whose body has felt the embrace of a giant Russian in a green and gold uniform, deftly reaches out to grab hold of bottles, rouge and razor.

In former times Lenin's umbrella was left to dry in the Café de la Rotonde, Lenin, who loved his old mother dearly, that passionate instinctive man who was later to emigrate to chattering Switzerland and then launch his revolution before ending up as an embalmed icon.

In Montparnasse mysterious Semitic peoples meet while you also come across women who hail from distant valleys, wrapped in mustard-coloured or bottle-green overcoats, protectively caring for young poets whom they reluctantly supply with flasks of spirits labelled with Nordic mottos.

The very smell of hot coffee is a source of joy for the desperate artists' models: women from Paris, Marseilles and Toulouse, who have some Breton, gypsy, or even Irish blood in them, who keep a little flame-coloured stray cat warm in their hands.

In central Montparnasse sensible or flighty young

English women with light-coloured eyes and strong calves live in little nineteenth-century houses behind flowering courtyards. They are fond of waterproofs and wear their evening dresses a little like a harness on their svelte bodies.

Police officers patrol in front of the Russian embassy where staff politely receive foreigners in reception rooms dating from the days of the devastated old empire. In the grey torpor of the Rue de Grenelle the lorry-drivers with their strong movements sometimes have a graceful dignity as they hold their bronze-moustached heads high. Meanwhile poets who work as managers, deputy managers or ordinary employees at the Ministry of Posts and Telegraphs have a quick glass of white wine at the bar inside the administration building. You can see them as they empty out on the pavement around six in the evening, sometimes knowledgeably observing the evening star.

The Avenue de Saxe is a profoundly desolate place filled with army smells. Those strapping, powerfully built, ruddy-cheeked fellows who have the ploughman's unwavering gaze and who walk along the avenue on a winter's day are lost young cavalrymen haunted by visions of their homeland's purple heather.

To get to morning mass families follow the pale walls of the École Militaire on the Avenue Lowendal, while a bugler from the country standing beside a sad puddle puts a brass trumpet to his lips.

In a sudden eddy of wind on the Place de Fontenay an officer spots his kepi blowing away, rolling along in the mud; it takes him a while to retrieve it because his sabre gets in the way. Inside an old sentry box that was once tricoloured, at the entrance to an adjoining building, a guardsman sits reading an old newspaper stained with gun grease. He has forgotten why he joined up and he counts the days over and over again.

The Paris Gates

In the new districts surrounding the main roads in and out of Paris, comfortable housing is being built for workers. There was so much hypocrisy and underhand dealing° involved in the fight against the slums but now a whole population aspires to living in bright apartments: the exhausted fairground wrestler covered in hieroglyphic tattoos, weary of this chaotic world, longs for walls painted in pastel colours.

An autumnal melancholy descends on the Porte de Bagnolet. The old people from the nearby home meet there, holding pinches of tobacco carefully in their tight fingers. They are often consumed by unspoken jealousies as they walk slowly, crushing the dry leaves underfoot.

On Boulevard Ney the barracks are more desolate than ever, the horses seem tired, but the bugle calls are the same as they were at the battle of Sidi-Brahim° when the trumpet sounded the charge instead of the retreat while Abd El Kader watched.

The old wine merchant who presides at his counter at the Point-du-Jour exit once saw a copy of Abel Hermant's novel *Le Cavalier Miserey*° smouldering on the barracks dung-heap. The cavalryman was holding himself stiffly on his horse, sabre drawn, ill-at-ease in his shako adorned with cocks' feathers.

At the Porte Maillot exit, Luna Park entices you into

the attractions; there are rides with river chutes, a merry-go-round with young boys going around on a quiet mare, games of skill where you are required to knock scantily clad ladies down from their perch where they lie yawning all day. Luna Park is full of rotten planks, worn grass and faded canvas; there's a whole flora there: spindly grasses, tiny mosses and minuscule mushrooms proliferate on the human attractions.

At the Porte de la Villette an abattoir worker covered in blood hails a taxi, abandoning his work, and leaves relying solely on the basis of an account that he has just been given without taking the time to call by his old concubine, in order to avenge his brother who was a disabled veteran of the battle at Mort-Homme and who was missing his family and friends down at the Vieux Port. The taxi takes him to the Gare de Lyon; that very evening he will be in Marseilles at the place that he knows.

At the Porte de Saint-Ouen where the impoverished edge of the city begins, there are still girls who throw stones at the person wandering through and others with sour-smelling hair who wear their camisoles loosely over their still-youthful bosoms while they pick up clients for a litre of wine.

Prosperous Districts

The servants from big houses go dancing in the evenings on the Avenue de Wagram alongside the travelling apprentice carpenters who come by once a year on their tour of France. When you head homewards to your lodgings on the outskirts and cross the district next to the Étoile there is nothing that delights you more than the compass rose. The grand houses tame the gust of wind that lifts your coat tails. In the porches there is nobody sheltering, and you feel that twinge of melancholy that also comes from pieces of music written for ensembles.

In the morning inside an imposing residence, through beautifully transparent glass, you can see the slender tree branches quivering and waving on the wide avenue. Many businessmen get out of bed in a saffron dawn to inspect their teeth, holding a mirror over their aging palates; as they wash following a strict routine they feel the coolness of silent water, the smoothness of marble and the sharpness of the blade. Their spirits are assailed by memories of autumn.

Some mornings, that troubling gentle stealth and cunning deal-cutting so dear to capitalism, which it occasionally manages to establish the world over, seems in Paris to mingle discreetly with birdsong and melodies played on an accordion. Even so, the fire at the earth's core forms new gemstones.

In the courtyards belonging to the big houses there is a fine moss set around the paving stones.

In apartments where winter cold never penetrates, eyes gaze intently into other eyes and exquisite clocks measure time, which makes its ravages felt on lungs, liver, heart and limbs.

Sometimes on the finest English cheviot-wool overcoat draped around an old man, there crawls a big striped, black and yellow caterpillar but he doesn't notice it.

Living a very prosperous life is a dream; you think of Balzac spending his nights shaping his characters according to human rituals, sitting amidst coffee aromas while his powerful breath crystallised on the cold windowpanes. You think of marvellous Baccarat glass on cutlery handles while the rain beat heavily on the windows of the Grand Hôtel Continental.

It's an opulent lifestyle with mirrors in bedrooms. If one of these big looking-glasses happens to be broken by accident or in anger, at the noise this makes, a shiver runs down beautiful spines, maybe the rosy back of a curvaceous courtesan, as she looks everywhere, under the clothes, under the bed, for a collar stud mislaid by her old lover.

Here the atmosphere is reminiscent of the time when girls handled the *louis d'or* coins that some veteran white-haired artists still like to include in their genre paintings. In rings, the pungent smoke from good-quality cigars wreathes around the mirror and window frames and overmantels forming that distinguished patina of age that could, sooner or later, easily end up being spattered with blood.

Along the last slopes of the Fortifications a young girl scarcely into puberty strolled along with a warrant officer on her arm; her highly polished shoes were gleaming and when he thought no one was looking he kissed his very young mistress several times.

The day was getting cooler, hoarse voices were coming from men sitting in a circle on the short grass who were cursing because they had accidentally knocked over a litre of dark heavy wine.

A man sat leaning against the wall of a wooden shack; you could observe that he was drawing diagrams, engrossed in mathematics, an observation that filled the dismantled Fortifications with magnificent poetry.

As the wanderer's footsteps echoed in this old defensible area, the sight of insect clouds around animal remains made him feel the presence of the simplest harmonies in the same way as Bernardin de Saint-Pierre once did.

Then the walker went up onto high ground to gaze at Paris spread beneath his feet. He could make out spires and towers. He identified the old Paris of horses and carriages with its solemn finely dressed valets, many of whom today lie buried in Champagne or Artois beneath wormeaten wooden crosses. He also identified the old criminal neighbourhoods. Using an old naval telescope, he located the green blur of the Buttes-Chaumont where the water is so still under the Suicides' Bridge. On the horizon in the opposite direction the fine structure of the Eiffel Tower reared up. Because they see it every day the stubborn soldiers serving their time at the École Militaire find it boring.

But the old naval spyglass left some things hidden at the heart and outer edges of Paris: Paris with its lilies, muck and gold, its inscriptions on columns or mouldings on grey houses, its women at café terraces wearing hats decorated with sprigs and flowers, or the hand turning the doorknob, or the glove being taken off to reveal the hand when the evening newspapers appear.

Dusk in Paris falls as ministers leave meetings and electric signs glow red. A lorry-driver, laughing about a trivial thing with his companion, says 'pull the string and the latch will go up'.°

Some people only view flowers as a prelude to love and are now anxiously looking for a florist in a deserted neighbourhood where sirens wail. Amid the rumble of buses under a pale sky, hearts respond to every sight and sound. Beneath it all they remember the delicious taste of fruit from a childhood orchard.

Paris brightly decked out for visiting foreign sovereigns is the image of the city that fills the dreams and imagination of the country lad whether he stands next to vast wheatfields or by fireside warmth.

When the arrival of big processions is announced, proud modest widows stop for a long time on the footpath, holding their blond child by the hand.

The Paris of the Universal Exhibitions is a beacon of

idealism and among the crowds of onlookers, who stare wide-eyed at the brightly coloured uniforms passing by, there are poachers from L'Indre-et-Loire whose scarred hands are washed by spring water.

Paris awaits the future with its graceful women, its enchanted evenings and its stolidly warm bar counters.

Young men try to elaborate clear visions, transported and elated as their footsteps ring out along the old avenues. Bright lamps coming on at night and the chance of eating a rich stew give many people renewed hope and joy.

The Paris houses wait too, still splendidly wedded to the earth, to the animals on its surface and the fauna in the ocean depths. People live and die behind their grey windows.

It's a night for caped overcoats, a furtive night. The Opera is bathed in purple light. The passers-by are going home to their beds and bourgeois monogrammed sheets.

Where have all the dawns gone? The duels with pistols drawn under trembling leaves while a Jesuit father, hidden behind a tree trunk, stood ready to absolve the big clerical-ist dueller determined to fight despite his beliefs? Where are the long rambles on horseback and on foot around the Ville d'Avray? The coachmen were waiting, half asleep near entrances with their lips curled and their leather britches sticking to grubby thighs; the exhausted horn players finished rehearsing around a big lamp still burning even though day was breaking.

The Elements: Water, Fire,
Fear, Lies, Enchantment, Tears

The families returning from visiting the lakes at Versailles stride across the Cour du Havre to catch buses that will take them home – older sisters, mothers and fathers carrying sleeping children in their arms.

Gazing at fountains, waterfalls and basins is a particularly pleasant pastime for nostalgic city dwellers, people like the brightly decorated soldiers from old garrisons who enjoy lying on their stomachs near the locks, chewing blades of grass.

In Paris the water-features in public parks induce a sense of calm and their basins, coated in the winter with a green or pink sheen, take on a supremely sumptuous appearance. Fires breaking out remind people living in the densely populated city that the forces of nature can rage at any time: not so many moons ago the Bazar de la Charité° went on fire along with all its great ladies inside while in cafés in the half-light young men kissed young women who were tightly laced into flowery corsets.

One day on the Place du Panthéon a brightly coloured balloon, decorated to look like a government minister, rose up into the air to the delight of students belonging to the national political parties. The town police looked on helplessly; a man shook his head sadly; in his buttonhole he was wearing a red Legion of Honour ribbon that bled into his serge jacket. He had practised the sabre in his day but without possessing all the relics that Rollo kept inside his sword hilt;° his hands were clenched inside red cotton gloves, a December sun shone, the windowpanes sparkled with frost flowers.

In Paris you can study the tiniest human gestures that leave a small trace in the universe: as a poor fellow strokes his very young girlfriend's hair you can see the lights from a street corner reflected in his spectacle lenses.

In a military outfitters', a student from Saint-Cyr buys the special white and red feather decoration for his shako. He is shown several samples, one particularly pleases him as he carefully strokes its feathers.

A bus driver, when the bus stops, signals to a fat hesitant lady that she can board; with a glance and joining both arms in a circle he communicates to her that if she stays standing on the platform at the back, the curved rail where passengers have just moved away will protect her stomach from jolts if she leans closely against it.

With a pounding heart, the young man striving to make his way in the world feels like a nervous, anxious schoolboy again while he waits outside important people's offices near a typist dreaming of her lovers. On the wall hang calendars, lists, maps and diagrams. The young man is holding his old yellow kid gloves, already shiny, oily and grimy from his first years in working life. Detached indifferent secretaries intimidate him, brushing past him swiftly as he looks out at the street battered by wind and sun. He sees the heavy green buses filled with clusters of people and sometimes the bus is followed by a solitary old man in a drab overcoat running to catch up with it. Unconsciously, the young man touches the cool marble mantelpiece that reminds him of a forgotten thirst.

In this beautiful Paris there are only lies, happy or sad. In a previous golden age when La Goulue° used to arrive at the Moulin-Rouge (wearing beauty spots and blood-red lipstick, in a coach and four, her dazzling fine-spun under-garments visible as she stepped down), in those days too the fertile medium of lies allowed false roses to bloom.

Not far from Place Gambetta, until very recently, in a little shack lit by paraffin lamps, lived an old lady who sold drink; in the middle of the room there was one round table, on the walls a map of France and an engraving depicting evening prayers on the bridge of a ship. When the regular customer who suffered from dropsy arrived, he would sit at the table in the company of old ladies in bonnets who drank white wine while he spoke with difficulty and at length. He used to describe the Hawaiian Islands, Easter Island, the Malay Archipelago, the Pontine Marshes, Tierra del Fuego, and recount his journey around the world in a sailing ship. Nobody could stop him from talking, he had to get to the end of his yarn. Finally, a longing for some turnip soup that was being prepared for him somewhere else would cause him to rise, walk slowly to the door, turn the doorknob, and let some lilac-scented air waft in. Then, once he had gone, the old lady would address her female customers: 'He's lying, it's all lies,' she would say.

While walking near the Canal Saint-Martin a middle-class man once heard whistles and then answering signals. He was gripped by fear in the rain that dampened his hat and overcoat, seeping into the dead plant cells in the hard felt and into the English fabric. At a nearby house a window-pane shattered, the man's blood stopped circulating and drained unseen from his suddenly pale skin in the darkness on that starless night.

Once he was home and warm, he threw some brochures and publicity leaflets into the wastepaper basket: advertisements for corsets, wine, steel fountain pens, and recovered his false chiselled mask-like expression.

Enchantment can assume thousands of forms. In the deconsecrated Notre-Dame cathedral, the Maillard girl,° dressed as the goddess Reason, found the smell of incense sickening yet she was happy because she could feel Chaumette's breath on her décolleté shoulders while he made a speech dressed in his revolutionary's jacket, red cap and white gloves beneath the blossoming rose window.

At the end of an artists' dinner I saw the countrywoman from the Rue Campagne arriving in evening dress, the same Auvergnat lady who cheerfully and energetically serves wine, coffee and liqueurs from behind her counter all day long; with her hair piled up high, more beautiful than ever (despite her limp because she twisted her ankle going down to decant wine in her cellar), her décolleté dress with black lace making her pale skin stand out even more, she was the toast of the evening. She was more reserved than at her counter, her face had softened and, brave as ever, she smiled at the ovations, soon rediscovering all the natural charm of her colourful language.

*

And so they go, seeking somehow to be moved to tears in public parks or busy streets, while catching the tram or the burning hot bus in August; or else climbing the thickly carpeted stairs to their doctor, or the bare stairs leading to their supplier and creditor. In the latter case, just before they reach the sixth floor, they hear him hammering a shoe, they imagine his forced grin, the opened litre of wine glowing red beside him, foreign furniture stacked around him. Much later one of these debtors will see his parish moneylender's apartment building being demolished and he'll feel tearful because the exposed inner walls will show wallpaper in different colours: salmon pink, sky blue, charcoal grey, all peeling off like layers of leaves.

A visual composition that appears cold overall can nonetheless move one to tears with a detail of a perfectly drawn calf or a finely executed ankle. Similarly, under the Paris sky you can feel your eyes grow moist just at the sight of a banker, a soldier, or a pimp, because their outlines and reactions are so clear and so perfectly authentic in the peaceful setting of the living street.

Time and the Hours

There is a theological abstraction about streets made bare by daybreak. Through a half-opened door, an aroma of coffee reaches you and fills the end of a street. Where paving stones have been lifted for roadworks, the earth is cracked and chapped the same way as it is in the fields.

The bread delivery woman tightens her black shawl across her chest, a shawl her mother made during the long evenings.

In a bar near Saint-Lazare station the waiter in shirt-sleeves with a napkin knotted around his neck is wiping down the nickel counters when a creature comes in looking for a very milky white coffee. Nobody can see that she is naked under a scratchy jacket. Poverty that she refuses to acknowledge is destroying her. She's spent all night in familiar haunts looking for a gentleman friend. She was asked to leave; she could hear the click of ivory balls on smooth billiard tables, so gentle, just like the old days.

At the Étoile metro station the trains have stopped: a man has just committed suicide; he wore red hunting gloves and had a dyed moustache that he sometimes used to chew, and the bitter taste of the dye was the taste of his whole life.

In some streets every kind of food produce spills over onto the footpaths; the hospitals and the prisons have been catered for earlier; now pretty or ugly housewives, whose movements are in tune with the stars, haggle over vegetables, fruit and meat.

At noon employees from the insurance companies, the Phénix, the Abeille and the Prévoyance, leave their offices. The shop-window displays are dazzling as daylight refracts into seven colours on the mirrors' bevelled edges.

In the afternoon women go out fully made up. Idlers rush to see attractions, such as the man fasting inside a glass cage; the sceptics discuss the phenomenon, one of them claiming that the man's clothes buttons are made of dried meat extract. Some ladies still go visiting the poor in the slums, just as the Empress Eugénie used to do.

Meanwhile, time that governs the phenomena of erosion, splitting and desiccation, keeps working away on wood, metal and stone. Water stagnates in park basins and heavy compost forms in the cracks on wooden benches where weeping widows sit, their white kid wedding gloves lying in distant bedrooms beside the boxwood darning egg used for repairing stockings.

In the theatres the red plush fades, in the evenings fleas jump around, even at gala performances, and insects bore through the busts of strong caryatids.

To experience the cool nights of his earlier life again, the uprooted countryman climbs right up to the little square not far from the Rue des Envierges. There are still many small well-tended gardens around it and sometimes the nightwalker, that unsettling but harmless presence who wanders these streets, catches sight of a bed of leeks revealed in a flash of lightning.

Couples come out of a cinema in a street lined with big houses; their heads are full of images of ladies in diamonds. A pigeon escaped from a laboratory, missing part of its spinal cord, totters on a pavement. Some cruel girls study him; one of them, exquisite as an Italian Madonna, has her arm in a sling because she was injured by a violent, amber-skinned lover.

On the boulevards and avenues, the breath that comes from those who sleep on benches displaces a dead leaf for a second. Deep inside cafés and in small dark hotels, people dream out loud.

The heavy vanilla aroma of high-quality chocolates, the kind you can still find in discreet tearooms, is only noticed by the stray dogs who enjoy a more sophisticated sense of smell than humans.

Harness bells on horses pulling the vegetable carts waken old beggar women who sleep lightly.

When it's four in the morning the lion tamer in his caravan at the Trône fairground° gets up to give the lion cubs asleep in his double bed their feed, a bottle of milk mixed with mineral water. His orange gold-braided jacket hangs on a nail. His wife is sleeping with her hair spread out on the ornately monogrammed pillow.

It's that time of night when Victor Hugo had his young maiden catch a chill as she was leaving a ball and transform, her whole body wracked by a burning fever, into a marble statue, because for the man who was the author of 'The Shadowy Mouth'° the bright blue of daylight always hid a dark underside; he was always haunted by splendid cold night air falling on angels' breasts.

*

On 31 December 1899 a few middle-class people were determined to stay awake to see in the exact moment that the century ended and, muffled up in scarves, on the stroke of midnight, they went out on their balconies for a little while to gaze at the sky heralding a new era.

Nightclubs and bordellos were jammed with pleasure seekers while in the churches midnight mass was being celebrated.

I love the empty Paris of August days. In the morning simple folk sit on dewy benches, people with low foreheads and grey wrinkled hands; it's only by accident that they live in capital cities and they go over and over calculations in their heads.

Meanwhile Mallarmé's faun° has come down from imaginary pastures and planetary woods and makes his appearance behind fronds of vegetation in cul-de-sacs and squares.

The laundries serve the needs of Paris in summer. The laundry women employ battalions of workers in white tops who have interminable conversations with their heads bent, most of the time about the dramatic goings-on in the neighbouring streets.

It might be one of these laundry workers, when she has gone back to her room and unlaced her dainty boots, who lies down in her dark blue skirt and white collar across the parquet floor, pressing her ear against it to hear a man's voice coming up from the floor below, the voice of the man she loves, a love that has less to do with his smile and more to do with the fine Westminster chiming clock that he watches over carefully, as a farmer guards his acres.

Streets

On a sunny day a yellow stucco façade can be seen where a sorrowful woman leans out at one of its windows.

In the street a police sergeant and some road workers are standing. Red wine from vines in the Hérault and Algeria flows in the wine bars where waitresses pearled with sweat laugh as they wipe down the oilcloths and scrub the pewter counters.

The single tree typical of Parisian courtyards is clad in that Île-de-France green that goes so well with the most sumptuous grey.

Conversations come from all sides. Vulgar expressions are so charged with life that you would like to strike up a friendly conversation with all those women who utter them just the same way when they're out on the footpath as they do at home beside their small, burnished stoves. In the air human odours mingle with smells of vinegar, onion and frying food that waft from open windows looking out on Sacré-Coeur, Notre-Dame, or a graveyard.

Every day a marvellous map of the sentiments can be chalked down on the bitter slate. On it should be listed the painted rose decoration above a brothel door in Grenelle at high noon, the obscure graffiti on a church wall in a district built in the Second Empire, the gesture of a suburban child who in a moment of joy beneath the sky, lays his dirty little palm with outstretched fingers on the burning wall.

★

Sad wanderers cast longing glances at sentimental post-cards, their shoe leather is wearing thin; hot or cold rain-water has made holes as big as sovereigns.

In squares that are green again mothers loosen their tops to feed their children, a section of silver braid shines on the park-keeper's tunic collar. In groceries assistants fill up grey bags with salt crystals. At her shop door the dairywoman sucks blood from a small cut on her finger. Locksmiths cut keys. Tripe merchants lay out calf hearts on marble.

Housewives with big eyes, delicate young wives whose satin skin is slowly becoming worn under woollen garments, purchase different chemical products at the dye merchant's: bleach, white soap stamped with cat's heads, soap marbled red or blue. On the café terraces in a sparkling aperitif a cordial briefly expands into a delicate cloud, a glass breaks, a child cries.

Silence fills a whole street where through a window you can see a young woman at her dressing table, her back bare.

Sometimes you are led into unremarkable streets that have no particular or recognisable charm, that are almost abstract, where night falls more simply and the hours are struck more distinctly, streets suddenly made famous by a mysterious murder.

In some streets where turn-of-the-century facades are ornamented by identical balconies, sad couples who live in garish interiors among faded furniture give themselves over to pleasures of the flesh: the evening newspaper lies open on a chair, mice nibble at a piece of Gruyère left on a saucer. All these things are part of the Parisian night while the wind whistles as it whistled in times gone by when the Royalist rebels used to go on reconnaissance missions under a starless sky.

It's good to stroll up these neutral streets with a friend where there is nothing to distract the eye. Under your feet you feel the reassuring arrangement of paving stones and then you both converse, you cheer each other up and start to draw fine distinctions and sort out your ideas; you barely hear a passer-by whistling, you barely notice a big greyhound following his master who is lost in thought, with the same nobility as he would follow him in some autumnal undergrowth.

Here in these streets, on these pavements, beneath the illuminated cigar signs at tobacconists that are about to close, you reaffirm the bonds of friendship and discuss some splendid image one more time while close beside you two policemen are revising for a promotion exam that demands a thorough knowledge of spelling, fractions and division with decimal points, but nothing at all about how the constellations move.

A man from Finistère walks along the Rue Réaumur. A smell of cooking fat drifts around the dwarf trees outside the cheap restaurant where there is a sign for silver-coloured soup. Office workers buy each other harmful aperitifs that provide traditional comfort. The Breton man heads towards the Temple pulling a short white pipe out of his pocket. From an ochre café where they have drunk lemon tea out of stemmed glasses Jewish salesmen emerge with suitcases full of gemstones, some have hidden wounds, others have escaped disaster; they wear suits cut from ordinary grey or brown fabric and none of them smoke. The silent Breton goes in to drink a white coffee while the Jewish men head off chattering towards the Rue des Rosiers, they plan to visit that fat woman who dozes almost all day long on a peony-coloured eiderdown, through rents in the silk, lifted gently by an evil-smelling puff of wind, clumps of eider down float away.

In the July heat a foaming runaway horse gallops down the Rue des Envierges. Children seek safety in the concierges' lodges. The little shopkeeper who wears a regional bonnet from the Berry startles from a daydream: she was remembering a day when strange coloured globes appeared around the sun and the viper that slithered towards the schoolmaster as he lay on his stomach in the little yellow wood, quite unaware of the danger.

A sergeant on leave jumps up to catch the horse at the same time as its rider is blithely shuffling cards in the Vielleuse café. On the big café mirror that was crazed by a shell during the war there is a painting of the vielle player with her black hair worn in coils.

Holiday Amusements

At the Trône Funfair a whole crowd of people listens to Pezon's° patter as he stands in his sky-blue, black-braided hussar's jacket; young girls arch their backs as they lean on the arms of supple men.

In the crowd somebody recognises the lion tamer; they once went to secondary school together; they greet each other warmly and Pezon gives his former schoolmate free admission.

The sky takes on a yellow tinge: a storm is brewing over Paris; blood boils in the bodies of young women in their prime as they tighten their lips in a great effort to appear calm; the lion tamer's niece smiles, the wild animals in their cages are distracted by the big flies that settle on off-cuts of brown meat. The observer's grey eye, set in its eye-ball veined with tiny red lines, captures a beautiful earthly composition: the menagerie's painted panels showing travellers being attacked by tigers, roller-coasters decorated with big snowy horses with golden shoes, the pink and white stand where strips of marshmallow hang, the gypsy fortune-teller's copper face. Alone in his straw hat among the crowds, the lower middle-class moralist secretly studies cold, sensual human hearts. His hazelwood cane that he varnished himself comes from the woods at Meudon, a bump in his waistcoat pocket indicates where he always keeps a ten-franc piece stashed away. At the sound of circus music his gloomy eyes brighten momentarily, the smell of chips bothers him. At last, the sun breaks through and lights up the pylons in a sparkly dust cloud on the Avenue du Trône.

Days of Rioting

We were eating when the riot broke out and we let the melting pear juice trickle down our throats. Down below in the street some very old women looked up towards the reddening horizon the way they used to when they were young during the Empire, thinking they could see soldiers' blood in the sky. A car driven by a chauffeur in a kepi was finding it hard to get through; a white dog with bright orange spots was sleeping alone in the back seat. In the Weber café women tore up bandages and they soon began to look like nurses. Some of them were delicate but others were muscular with strong forearms no longer tanned from the beach. A young journalist was carried in on a stretcher, a man with a moustache who had worked his way up on an evening newspaper. We used to know him in the Latin Quarter when he would spend days at a time simply doing nothing, not even living a debauched life, not eating, never complaining. Now he was covered in blood, unconscious, and holding his journalist's pass in his clenched hand. Everyone was getting worked up about the mobile police units charging the crowd. You could hear people all around talking about ex-servicemen, the Camelots du Roi,° the people's rights, even about gilded youth. The Ministry of the Marine was in flames, they said.

★

In the last century, the evening after a disturbance, a man was running as though he was being pursued by a horde of people but the only thing stirring around him was the foliage. However, near Père-Lachaise cemetery° the cavalry had just charged. One guardsman's sabre had decapitated a child returning home with a milk can, the earth in the paving stone cracks soaked up the poor milk and the murderous guardsman's face was spattered with red.

The next day the carpenters from Soubise and the apprentice with the puffy red eyelids were back standing on wood shavings. There was leek soup steaming in everyone's bowls; from the bistro across the way a man came out gesticulating; in splendid old age he was known as Clémentine's Dad and at nearly sixty-five he lived with a young woman skilled at making Alençon lace, a gorgeous girl with a dazzling smile, extremely healthy though her bosom was kept carefully concealed.

Girls

On bad days, when spongy shoes become saturated with muddy water, they wait with their good-quality strong-ribbed umbrellas. They accost single passers-by, or groups of three to four men belonging to a visiting overseas wind orchestra who are looking for a doorway to shelter under, the rain dripping from their caps emblazoned with a silver lyre.

In the Chapelle area the girls are on the lookout at the entrances of small hotels designed for brief encounters; the hotel fronts are often decorated with green and pink tiles that never get damaged or discoloured by the rain. Out of chocolate-coloured brothels massive men appear sometimes quite unabashed, under blue, silvery-grey or tawny skies. Deep inside small misty or sunlit cafés that are decorated with fading lilies, some of their little flowers turning brown, puny men with white hands and extraordinarily ringed fingers shuffle kings and queens under an *œil-de-boeuf* window.

One girl goes home; her complexion is fading but good for another few years – according to those who have evaluated her for profit. What childhoods haunt her? What journeys on dazzling roads where red-faced road workers drank beside piles of white stones, what mean or mischievous grandfather raising his stick in a sunken lane, who stopped to listen to a blackbird?

She turns the door handle at the bistro-restaurant-hotel: Hôtel du Cantal or Hôtel de la Nièvre; the man is waiting for her with a bottle, a big plate and a dozen oysters before him. The manager looks at her surreptitiously, he wears a cardigan, carries a floor cloth, and keeps an eye on everything. The male customer stays silent, and the woman orders cheap dishes. He will only open his mouth in the bedroom when it's time for some well-aimed blows and then to launch into recriminations: the other evening, why did she prevent him from swiping that plump meaty chicken?

On Boulevard de la Chapelle you sometimes meet the smooth-faced man who wears gold pince-nez. He walks through evil-smelling air whose imperceptible eddies are governed by fixed laws: coal and wool dust, rice flour, dead skin; he stops to look in the window at a second-hand shop; he sees a certificate of good conduct awarded to a Zouave infantryman, a copper table stove and a sword corroded with verdigris; it starts to drizzle, one by one the girls' umbrellas go up and he carefully puts up his own.

Does the man want to meet one of those shapeless neurasthenic brunettes and gaze deep into her eyes, women who sigh as they lace up their high boots but no longer tremble when regiments go by?

On summer evenings when the sun has heated the asphalt and the locomotives leaving the Gard du Nord puff their smoke towards a horizon filled with red dragons and gathering storms, the homeless adolescent goes to sit on a bench in the Square de la Chapelle. He looks at the poor women dozing, the deserted girl wearing cheap jewellery, the big, tall, sometimes very fragile prostitutes who brush past the railings. Once he has rested, he drifts off into the surrounding streets: the shoemakers smell of leather, the butchers smell of blood and the laundry workers of light perspiration.

The girls on the Boulevard Richard-Lenoir have lovely slang. When the passer-by spurns their offer, they spontaneously shout: 'Ah! Clear off, you meadow midget!' It's a circumlocution to describe a cow.

Those on the Rue de la Harpe often seem tired and plaintive, they are more reserved. One of them, from Brittany, always felt the cold and didn't know how to read and was a regular at a little restaurant on the Rue Saint-Séverin where all she wanted to eat was roast chicken because she claimed that any other food made her feel nauseous.

As for the girls on the Rue Saint-Denis, they are well-known and accepted in their neighbourhood, and at certain gentle times of day when they converse in doorways, they conjure up images of simple country life: the peacefulness peculiar to cities can often feel like being in the countryside among birds' nests as they are about to go to sleep.

Some of the women soliciting in this street wear the pleated skirts typical of the Markets paired with high, red-heeled boots; on their days off from the game they arrange to have their children, who are being brought up outside Paris, sent to them and they go to the wash-house to wash their linen. Many of them are self-employed and have no pimps. The women working at the Markets speak to them politely. Of course, some are loud-mouthed and insolent and lift their skirts up in anger, but others remain very quiet. They are extremely wary and sensitive to the seasons and are most reluctant to leave their neighbourhood.

On Boulevard du Montparnasse, at the Madeleine, and in Montmartre the girls wear hats and can be classed as part-timers. Some get to *escape*. In some cafés in Montmartre whole gangs of them make themselves scarce, shouting together.

Women

In the beginning they all look the same and you tell your-self that it's more important to get to know the city first and that one day you'll meet them and get to talk to them. Later when years have passed, you notice the gentle breath of one of them as she arranges her hair in a mirror in the street. She is wearing a perfect dress that shows her at her best; her face doesn't look particularly intelligent, but she's carefully made up with rouge and powder, simply follow-ing city custom. Another day you start to notice them all living around you. There is a disconcerting variety in how they dress. Some radiate a stunningly modest elegance; you pass them in the suburban centres where preoccupied housewives are carefully selecting what meat and vege-tables to buy, creatures from every province in France min-gling with women whose faces and bodies are obviously from Italy or Spain.

In the densely populated areas, many women pass by on the hilly streets, women who live surrounded by the odours of onions and Sunday washdays that rise up from the courtyards. They mask these odours with cheap scent and sometimes when they want to keep their souls pure, they put on an expensive perfume that no lover has given them. Others are just as happy in the neutral odour of mod-ern buildings. All of them just as they are: bootmakers, seamstresses, stooping manicurists, window dressers who crouch for long periods during the day and stand up so straight in the evening, all of them still so healthy in the twilight, walking home to their lodgings, young women or wives in streets descended from heaven.

At the end of a day when a storm has been brewing the seamstress's apprentice goes home, climbing nimbly to the landing on the fifth floor that is bathed in a murky sunset. The concierge yells from the depths of a courtyard, a child's trumpet plays, his mother hushes him sharply.

Then only the sound of the sewing machine filters out beneath the scuffed door belonging to the woman who works from home.

Her room is filled with photographs. At the Louvre she saw the Regent, supposedly the biggest diamond in the crown. Is it real? Is it fake? Her father says it's fake as he drinks his absinthe in the evenings in the baking heat or the biting frost.

What venom, base self-interest, or stupidity motivates some of those petty, arrogant women employed in government offices that makes them target their young colleagues and pick on them? The conversation always goes something like this: 'Well, my dear, you're looking very healthy today', or else: 'I wouldn't wear sleeves like that if I were you.'

If they have lunch in the office each one complains about the other who 'is taking up her space' or 'eating smelly food'.

And then they make a point of competing about their husbands' sexual appetite, about when and how often.

You would like to be able to dash off sketches of scenes like these and colour them with a sad wash; they are part of the tragedy of Paris. Sometimes it happens that nobody comes to see the serious woman to take her by the hand, but she always finds a reason to be cheerful and even when she's living in the most horrible dump, she consoles herself with hope. Nobody has the time to give her jewellery or clothes or tend her carefully like a vine.

Many middle-class girls hide a life of passion secretly within themselves. With clean bodies and a jaunty step, they cross the parks, their nails neatly manicured and varnished with a tiny brush. They're going to meet their lovers in anonymous bedrooms.

They struggle with men everywhere: in buses, on washroom staircases, where hands with red hairs on them land on their shoulders, and in quiet streets in Passy where sons of boorish gardeners still live. They come home when the lamps are shining on the set tableware; over the course of a day a light film of wind-borne grime has settled on them.

For the woman history scholar who smoothed her Mona Lisa hair in a fragment of broken mirror, whose brains were fried from too much study, Charles V, upon whose empire the sun never set, was posthumously an object of tender devotion.

When she was very young, sitting on the stone benches in the park at Auteuil, she used to watch the tree surgeons carefully cutting away side shoots not far from the cloches that contained shining melons, but now she is just a laughing-stock for the café regulars. She wears a big hat with flowers, dresses in pink velvet and sometimes puts little pieces of ice on her tongue. In the past, when she wasn't rambling and lost in the drawing rooms at the Continental, she used to show young people the marks that her bracelets made on her wrists and arms. She used to hold little teacups between her fingers so delicately that young men in silk hats would be overcome with emotion.

Once she went home through very quiet streets on the arm of an elderly gentleman and quivered when a whinnying horse broke the silence.

People and Life

There is a whole tribe of people who wear small jewellery, who speak with reedy, nasal, or stubborn voices. The men drink in a ritual way and express themselves in aphorisms. The women chatter at the wash house or the grocery.

This nation is sometimes charitable but can just as often carefully cultivate burning resentments. They are day labourers or artisans, without religious belief or real political allegiances, who enjoy complex jobs and elaborate adornment and are not put off by sour or strong smells. Early in the morning they shake hands that are covered with coal dust or bronze filings.

In the opulence of Paris these are the people who make you forget about theories or systems and instead focus on beautiful objects alone, for example, a large, ribbed glass, so thick that you can drop it from a height onto the floor where it will roll without breaking, or a deep smooth plate bordered with a fine blue line.

To this group belong snowy-haired women who are neither young nor old, who work in toy manufacturing.

Inside their lodges the concierges still live among their knick-knacks and cats. The stew simmering on the cooker gives out steamy smells that seep through cracks in the wall and gaps in the floorboards. The wireless spreads news from around the world, famous speeches, less magical than the gossip on the grapevine that the housewives peddle to the concierge on rainy evenings. They talk while their husbands grow bored, waiting for leek soup in the tiny dining room where the old parents died.

At that very moment, alone in his cold room above the concierge's lodge with its pungent warmth, a young man is thinking about the kings of Judah and Solomon's riches. He happens to be from country stock, is well-built, and wears woollen fabrics that were once good quality.

The salt of the earth fill the streets. Carrying shopping baskets, their shirt cuffs protruding from shiny silvery-black jackets, they peer short-sightedly at displays in grocery shops that sometimes have baroque names: *The Rabbits' Tomb, Martyrs' Food Store.*

These men can often be seen standing up straight in the back row of a photograph, with their benevolent moustaches and hands resting on small tables; at that minute the cavalry was passing by the window, but it wasn't the right time to look out, they had to keep staring at the camera lens.

What a Chinese landscape we had strayed into that evening. A delicately painted sky was slowly changing around us. A little house with a garden caught the subdued light.

The square next to Place Gambetta was unfurling its yellow foliage while a smell of blackcurrant wafted from a chemist's shop. A woman came out of it, her perfect figure visible under her dress. In his dispensary the pharmacist was mixing powders flavoured with julep.

One after the other men came to sleep on the benches.

Their jacket linings were still intact. Their bodies settled; sometimes a leaf fell on them.

Cyra was a great drinker of bitters. When he was young his friends had TB; because he was a gentle giant full of bravado, to show that he had no fear of catching their illness he drank their mucus in a cocktail always in the following proportions: two thirds Picon to one third Gentian.

One noon in winter, Cyra with his white Gaulish moustache went into his wine dealer's wearing a raspberry-coloured pullover tight over his torso. He sat down in front of a bottle and some hot food and from under his shirt took out a dying sparrow that he had picked up in the snow and placed next to his heart. He tried to revive it by gently giving it beakfuls of bread.

Everyone knew that Cyra was tough, and nobody let their true feelings show; he cut short any signs of approval by saying, 'I like these little creatures, they're Parisian delinquents.'

His efforts came to nothing, so he put the bird back against the warmth of his chest and ate silently for a while before taking him out in the hollow of his hand, attempting to revive him again.

The red-hot stove was roaring when the manager who was busying himself at the tables could restrain himself no longer and although he respected Cyrano he intervened with a shrug: 'Chuck it in the fire.'

But Cyrano raised his head, lifting an eyebrow:

'Ah, how about I threw *you* in there?' he replied, tucking the still inanimate little animal into his bosom.

'You can't throw me in, I'm too big,' said the manager.

'Don't worry, I would cut you into pieces to put you in,' Cyra assured him.

Just then, through the opening of the pullover the sparrow, suddenly revived, flew out.

The great drinker of bitters caught him mid-flight, went to release him in the courtyard, came back, saying to everybody: 'I gave him his freedom, 'e's like us, 'e's entitled.'

Under a gas burner, the pimp with the silk cap was shuffling queens, kings and the knave of hearts. Today he calls the queen the woman: isn't there the woman of diamonds, a bit shrewish, the woman of hearts with her flowery throat, the woman of clubs with the shapely ankle? And this scene is really playing out in the present in a Gare du Nord setting. You can hear the trains whistle as they leave for Calais. At the Square de la Chapelle, women breastfeed their babies. Old bloodstains harden, crackle, fall and decompose under the cast-iron pillars of the overhead metro. Gathering around street singers there are groups of girls in dark red blouses and young airmen who haven't yet had the baptism of a flight but who are driven by secret demons and the spirit of adventure. They no longer draw on the tables with spilt wine the way their ancestors the mercenary knights used to do, but they envy the parade uniforms that the knights would wear in non-temperate climates, with cuffs in a discreet blue or a finely woven white.

Secret passwords are always handed down the generations; however, it seems that the era of famous crimes is no more and that villains are no longer so easily identifiable now.

One thug from the Place Maubert once took pleasure in killing a passer-by for no reason, other than that he was whistling and got on the brute's nerves; pals in the mob would sit down in their barber's chair and calmly set their Browning down on the marble.

Nevertheless, young men from the underworld continue to make a living; they like the childhood taste of sticky sweets: red cherry drops, tricoloured rock, liquorice shoelaces, gums shaped like medals with generals' heads on them. The destiny of the women who sold them the sweets in the little grocery-cum-haberdashery shops hangs by a slender thread.

Their lives follow their course: between two jobs they exchange gold signet rings, they drink Vichy water and spirits, or borrow a light from the Algerian cavalryman who walks through the bar while his mistress cries, curled up in a corner.

They treat each other to quiet seaside holidays. You can see them there lying in the sun, yawning; sometimes when they breathe in the briny air, they remember an old taste for honesty.

One small landlord takes a liking to the neighbour on his landing and confides in him: 'When I go out walking, I have my hands behind my back, they're white and people say: "He's a landlord, he has white hands".'

He was once a cobbler and keeps his black jacket clean, but there is an odour that clings to him because he is extremely miserly and never sleeps in sheets but wears old clothes instead and wraps himself in blankets.

One day he was taken to see a doctor to whom he

confessed: 'You know, doctor, I am a virgin, I still have the heart of a twenty-year-old.' He walks the streets for days on end, from Vaugirard to the Buttes-Chaumont or to Batignolles and back. His neighbour lent him a book about Joan of Arc, written by a would-be prophet; he returned it with a little sing-song reply: 'Oh! That's not what history is, no, that's not history.'

He only goes to the theatre on the Fourteenth of July when admission is free. In thirty-three years, he has only received one single letter. He has a vivid memory of someone once treating him to a cup of coffee.

The solemn stupidity of human beings, their gentle emotions, their short-lived fraternity, the way they bless themselves when they cross over fords in wide landscapes lit up by flashes of lightning. In a family-run guest house in a small Breton town you see these old maids in ornamental blouses licking small chicken bones with false refinement. They end up talking about the relative merits of herbal teas: you need two flower heads per person for camomile, lime blossom is much too bland. Through the open dining-room window you can see incredible mists floating on the countryside; in the foreground gooseberries with diseased leaves grow beside sweet pea and sweet william.

They will go back to Paris with their heads completely empty. They will live there frugally without leaving their neighbourhood until July warms up the paving stones again. It will be their lot to suffer from delusions or maybe skin conditions that will make other customers edge away from them in the little restaurant where a poster of gentian pickers hangs on the wall.

Returning to her room in the Rue Berthe, one of these spinsters was to get a terrible shock when she saw the body of a man, dressed in the loose-fitting uniform that road-menders wear, stretched out on some waste ground where he fell asleep in death, sick and alone with a blade of grass between his teeth.

Two Paris Bistros

There was a bistro on the Rue de Vaugirard called *The Great Comet of 1811*. The first owners of the business who had come from some arid province were contemporaries of this comet and saw its tail at the same time as their thoughtful son was camping on the plains of central Europe.

A widow who wore her hair in a large grey bun ran the Comet. She was called The Mother; her clientele consisted almost exclusively of young people who fancied themselves as artists. She always employed very young serving girls who received free board and lodging but no pay, who ended up in that demi-monde that still survives in the Latin Quarter. On long afternoons while The Mother smoked a cigarillo and played cards with two or three of her customers, you could sometimes see one of her girls warding off the men's advances, holding a calendar advertising 'Amer Picon' across her chest by way of a shield.

One of the most reliable Parisian bistros still exists on the Rue Chanoinesse. It's called *Le Vieux Paris* and was formerly known as *The Cross of Lorraine*. The owner, a small stocky man from Burgundy, is a principled person who always trains his dogs well and who shaves off his hair every summer. His wife helps him; she has a distinguished face and bearing and wears a white chignon. He can have deep affection for his family and friends but doesn't like to show it. In his home province where he only returns rarely to visit his elderly parents, his name is mistakenly engraved on a war monument to the dead of 1914–1918; during that war he was a chauffeur to General Mangin and travelled as far as the Balkan coast and when he was there, he tasted omelettes made from giant turtle eggs. From his window, while he eats one of the cheeses that he has prepared and macerated in his own homemade alcohol, he can look out at the towers of Notre-Dame in mist or in sunlight; he knows the bell-tower fauna and gives out about how increasingly rare the swallows have become; every three to four years he makes a point of mentioning another person who has thrown himself from the top of the cathedral; he sells good single varietal wines.

At the Vieux Paris, there's still a whole collection of old glassware from fin-de-siècle Paris bistros ornamenting the shelves: enormous thick-fluted glass measuring cups that can roll on the floor without risk of breaking, broad-bottomed spirit tumblers with fine ribs. Nowadays when the *plat du jour* is served, the old coffee cups with their curved, blue-lined rims are used as mustard pots.

There is a period quality to the magnificent pewter counter with its border of vines; the water tap is topped by a bronze figure of a reaper; the wall mirror at the back is decorated with a Directoire Style motif. In a fish tank set into the wall there are little fish from the Seine donated by sailors and members of the river police.

During the hours when the owner sleeps, sometimes to be abruptly wakened by the growl of a dreaming dog, this Paris bistro is bathed in wonderful silence; meanwhile in the Marais over on the other side of the river, a ninety-year-old revisits the royal flowerbeds.

Priests

Sometimes you see unkempt old priests picking up shiny objects as they go about the streets: a piece of tinfoil or a nail. One of my female friends was amazed that nobody bothered to put them in a home, considering they were damaging the reputation of the clergy. I told her that Catholics saw them as ministers and spiritual guides and people were reluctant to make them go to retirement homes if the priests themselves refused to go there.

Besides, it seems that many Parisian priests choose to turn a blind eye to the visible suffering around them. How often you see that greedy calculating look they have in the metro when they try to spot an empty seat! Now the only ineffable thing about them are the very fine gilt-edged pages of the breviaries that fuelled our daydreams when we were children.

Even so, you can still sometimes see a learned ecclesiastic crossing over the Pont des Arts under a spring or autumn sky and raising his hat as he gives two or three coins to the accordionist beggar.

They are friendly, the sturdy young curates who come from the country to work as locum priests during the summer. To take advantage of what the city has to offer they sometimes go to the circus together because the circus, unlike the theatre, is not out of bounds for the clergy. They have finished their military service where they often commanded authority; in the bunkrooms they would remain expressionless and calm despite their comrades' vulgar language and they always were ready to help and nobody prevented them from kneeling down beside their beds to pray in the evening.

As well as being home to extremely charitable priests or others who are simply bureaucrats, Paris also harbours the immoral priest who might or might not have been properly ordained and the bad priest turned moneylender; on an evening when a storm threatens, and the fire engine's mournful siren can be heard passing below the windows, he offers you a possible commission for selling the chalice from his first mass.

Trades

At noon, near the river at the Île de la Cité market the nurserymen, their agent and the man who sells protected species of birds are all in a calm mood. They take out big knives and cut up bread and cold meat.

At the same time, the delivery men from the Bazar de l'Hôtel de Ville steady their rearing horses and get down from their vans to go to the bistro; now they're talking about the frost that is going to damage the seedlings in their suburban plots. The chair-repair man's donkey brays, his master sounds his horn, but the fine mist still lingers.

Flower sellers offer violets to rich gentlemen. The taxi driver stamps his feet under the frosty trees. He is pleased with the warm comfortable layer provided by the big brown sweater that his mother knitted for him during the long days, as she occasionally looked up at the water flowing under the Pont de Grenelle.

One indelible vision is the sight of the rag-and-bone man full of warm wine poking his stick into the bins. The tribe of rag collectors eats and drinks well; while rags are becoming scarcer Paris is still full of flashy riches. The rag collector knows this; he is aware of false gemstones, yet for a split second he is dazzled by a herring's head, old gold and bronze. He can sense when gales, storms, and bright spells are brewing.

*

The bakery trade preserves old customs and practices: the apprentices' bicycles are sometimes decorated with miniature shovels. The bakers' coat of arms is as follows: *on a field sable two oven peels argent charged with gules three loaves*; and on the arms specific to the Faubourg Saint-Germain bakers: *azure with Saint Honoré or holding in dexter a crook the same and in sinister a baker's peel argent charged with gules three loaves.*

The women who work in bakeries are elegant and friendly and dusted with fine flour; the mean ones, the cripples and the bullies are all softened by the flour that clothes my own bakery lady in gentleness. She washes herself very slowly, very carefully, in front of the bright or gloomy window; she has no fear of eczema or sores; if she gets them, she accepts them like stigmata.

The saddlers' craftsmanship can be of the highest quality, you can see an example of this on the Rue des Martyrs. The saddler here stitched fine leather saddles all day long; when evening came, he drank a lot, never aperitifs, not even spirits, always red wine. When he went back to his room pickled in cheap red wine, he lay down fully clothed and let his cap drop limply from his hand down by the side of the bed. He would sleep the whole night through and when dawn broke, he would wake gently and carefully pick up his cap, put his feet on the floor and return to work. He was so skilled that he was invited to go to America; he went, and he died there – the people in his neighbourhood claimed that it was during Prohibition – in a very comfortable hospital under foreign skies far from home.

*

The Freemason typographer has a long, fine, blonde beard. Rumblings caused by badly fried food constantly growl in his intestines. His black overalls against the pewter counter where he's drinking, next to the cream dress worn by an unknown curious passing customer, combine in a subtly harmonious composition similar to the different complex flavours that strong wines can acquire at the day's end.

Suburbs

The wedding buses coming back from Robinson after nightfall all belong to different companies and each bus tries to go faster than the next, overtaking as the drivers get caught up in the game.

Along the route, trees white with flowers glow; in the bus a gold chain is stretched across a silk dress: a grandmother wearing an old-fashioned jewelled necklace.

These suburbs have gardens; from morning to evening they are a hive of confused activity. Around nine in the morning you see the edge of a round table with a big white bowl and a croissant with a bite taken out of it. Cyclists have disappeared into the silvery mist. An angry dog growls behind the iron gates of a villa.

At midday a couple laboriously chew in front of some ornamental stuffed birds on a mantelpiece. The doctor comes in; his clothes seem brown because his trousers, woven in three different threads, are spattered in mud. He recognised the house by its ochre shutters and its sulphur yellow roses.

On winter afternoons there's a man, a litigious ex-priest, who comes out to get a breath of fresh air on his doorstep, wearing gold spectacles perched on his nose. At precisely that moment his former student arrives, a man worn out by late nights, hunger and sore eyes, and the older man who still has more authority holds out his arms encased in tight-fitting black sleeves. They meet up the way they used to do in the wicked grey city at the hour appointed for truculent theological debates, when chubby well-manicured index fingers (sometimes one finger would have a blackened nail) would settle on encyclical texts; the bishop had cold stony blue eyes and a scent of tobacco clung to him. The master and pupil greet each other with a kiss, somewhere a cock crows, a delivery van rattles on the dry road and around them the Paris suburbs appear infinitely pure.

When evening comes, in elegant post offices bright hair shines behind the counters, many post office ladies have kept themselves pure despite the filthy telephone conversations they overhear between villa owners who are intent on debauchery and carousing in time-honoured fashion; there are, however, many post office women who become tainted early on but the woman I want to tell you about, when she gets home to her bedroom with its scent of musk and dried violets, at last lets her hands fall by her sides as she stands in front of her proud cheval mirror, but not for long because her fingers which have worn the same rings for the past twenty years toy sadly with the lace on her bosom where she lowers her head and her firm double chin.

The lights come on gently in the suburbs; the last lamplighter's uniform with its red braid is stirred by the evening breeze. In old households, meals are orderly, the cat miaows as the cream soup, chops and fromage blanc slowly make their appearance on the table; the sound of a trombone comes from a little house and a turtle dove can be heard cooing.

In the night the dandyish prodigal son tries to proposition the dark-haired servant girl in her bedroom with its poplar-wood furniture; when she refuses there is a struggle; the Breton servant wrestles with the strength of a powerful archangel.

In the trains young widows hold their children and giant bouquets on their laps, slightly plump women with bright kindly expressions and small veiled hats perched on their blond hair. Then the last rays of the sun expire, the thin clumps of trees grow dark; the stations pass by with their winking lights that sometimes reveal gravel, small buildings, flowerbeds.

At Villennes-sur-Seine, boys and girls with bare arms and legs climb up into the compartment laughing and singing.

The suburbs conceal private chapels and stolen or abused children. Beneath the horizon where Paris lights are reflected against the sky there are roses at Fontenay and, further away, factories that make stained glass and further still, rust-coloured kitchen gardens where at ground level the beets pop out their green stems.

Last Visions

A hail of beans falls into the paper bag held in the sinewy hands of an old woman wearing a moon-coloured petticoat. Sardine tins are treacherously attractive; when he opens them with the key that is always too small, the poor fellow who eats alone in his room sometimes injures his hands and gets a nasty cut. A small, feeble, highly strung person almost sees red when he hears a tube of macaroni snap, as hard and brittle as his next-door neighbour's arteries, the neighbour who gesticulates with his long hands.

In damp streets where stalls are laid out, fish gleam with a slight ammonia smell; cabbages with lymphatic juices are heaped in baskets, because these products are also used as fertiliser. At the entrance to a dark corridor a second cousin from the country makes an appearance, biting into a raw carrot.

On the banks of the Seine an old man shaves his friend who has glowing golden skin. The old man was a carpenter in Flanders and after years of skilled joinery work his gestures are precisely human and his gaze direct. Near them, a man sleeps with his fingers interlinked behind his head, the city cradling him like a careless mother. Scenes such as these release feelings of tenderness in the human frame, unleashing harmonies: the soaring Louvre buildings, the twisted leaning trees, the whispered fraternal conversations on the Pont d'Austerlitz where unemployed people skilfully build little stone houses.

In one of the side chapels in Saint-François-Xavier, at vespers at the stroke of three, the two sacristans have just sat down, side by side, and they chat as if they were in a café. One holds his pommelled cane between his legs while the other has placed his across his knees.

In their everyday uniform, black overcoats with plain epaulettes and red trim, they look like people in a painting by Daumier, and he might have depicted them smoothing their bushy paternal moustaches alongside the three theological Virtues shown with feet and hands bound.

Paris still has little café-hotels that have mirrors etched with amphoras, exotic birds and flowers, places that the guests love because it is only here that they are really held in high esteem.

In one of those furnished apartment buildings where so many couples mill about, near the counter in the bar downstairs a parrot flutters, a bird with the softest grey plumage who is trained to repeat old obscenities. When he's silent the parrot chews sunflower seeds; the owner's son studies a book; inside his skull it seems that, the more he reads, a fine lacy network begins to form.

This is where Fernand and Julie live. Fernand is often at his window. Sometimes you can see him turning a daisy around in his fingertips while with pursed lips he whispers as he removes each petal: 'I love you a little, a lot', nodding his head while the wind ruffles the wild chest hair exposed in the V of his shirt. Julie used to work for silk farms in the

Dauphinois region and met Fernand in his gunner's uniform one day at noon when strips of sunlight shone on the wide avenue in a small garrison town; that day he treated her to a vanilla ice-cream along with a kiss that filled her with a mingled scent of leather, wine and metal.

A cobbler emerges from a hidden booth and crosses the Champs-Élysées. Purely by chance, he witnesses a collision between a private car and a taxi. When the taxi driver is accused of being at fault, the cobbler defends him vehemently despite having seen nothing, and supremely confident in his black leather apron, his hands black, his back stooped, his hair grey, he shouts over and over again in a quavering voice: 'A taxi driver is not a slave, a taxi driver is not a slave'. Because it is Memorial Day little American flags flutter on Claridge's facade.

In the metro, a puffy, red-eyed child, in the care of an enormous solidly built mother, sings, laughs, sticks out his tongue and scratches himself.

This woman carried ten children inside her, some were born in Clichy, some in Levallois, others on the Rue du Commerce. She counted cauliflowers in the bluish-pink first light. She comes in and out of Paris where the breezes blow. You could imagine her as an allegorical figure, drinking cold water from Wallace Fountains° in the depths of winter. Above her, planes that will cross the Great Wall of China fly high overhead.

French Publisher's Note (2006)

The republication of this book, *Paris*, meant a lot to Jean Follain because he believed that it occupied a central, if not obvious, place among his works. Two months before his accidental death he had decided to revise the text. We have completed this second edition carefully following his instructions.

In the same spirit we thought it would be interesting to include two short unpublished texts in this volume, both starting points for the same project. The first, written in ink on notepaper from the Dupont-Barbès brasserie (in an area where Jean Follain lived at the time) mentions a future book whose title was to have been *A Day in Paris*; it dates from 1930. The second, titled *Preliminary Notes*, is from the first months of 1934.

Two Unpublished Extracts

A Day in Paris

I plan to write a book called *A Day in Paris*.

I wake in the morning around five o'clock, at cockcrow. Intoxication is over and there's no sense of shame. For a moment a rosy, red orchard lights up the walls. Then grapes and peaches melt from it. Native sun, native sun (see Natal and Nepal in the geography books), you are no more! Oh grandmother, grandmother, to describe you a person would have to be a human genius with the gift of simple language.

If the late Jarry, or P. Mac Orlan, Salmon and Jacob weren't in the world, what would become of us?

The curtains that my mother gave me hang dismally. There is no coffered ceiling. There are no swallows painted there either.

The lopsided marble dressing-table is there, solemn and stern, a lopsided Venus of Milo; no woman looks at herself in the mirror, stretching her arched body with two spreading softish bluish breasts, bluish.

Everything is dirty from the razor to the toothbrush. A pretentious toilet-set designed to look aristocratic calls to mind the Second Empire, *Civil Servants' Wives*, Courteline° and Delobelle.

Everywhere hearts are held by visceral threads. Books lie around: *Phèdre*, Bossuet, *Le Chevalier des Touches*, Veuillot° the cooper's son, defender of primogeniture and of Rome against Paris, Veuillot who was prone to bitter tears. The dissolute morning light gently creeps in; pure dawn is dead. Imaginary manicure tools, combs, painful fine-tooth combs, combs going all the way back to childhood gleam and live on in memory.

The sponge from the Passion oozes cool water, only in the imagination, unfortunately.

Silky bodies so far away on roads that traverse the world. When I hunger for them too much, when I hunger too much for a monumental life of stellar achievement, I call to mind a gun held to my lilac temple, I call to mind a hemp rope hanging from an iron ring fixed to the anthracite grey ceiling, but the thought of suicide never occurs to me.

Preliminary Notes

In the days when the child pored over an old map from the Universal Exhibition of 1878 and would go on imaginary journeys, the sound of wind rustling the leaves had a rare quality but it didn't block out the clock's ticking. The wind added a marvellous melancholy mingled with a lust for life and adventure.

Every Paris arrondissement° was tinted in lovely pastel colours; somewhat to my annoyance – I was a highly strung, clumsy child – the old map would not fold out properly and broke at the folds. Sometimes during storms, a tile would fall from a roof. There were many thatched roofs covered with flowering bushes and people said that during cyclones some of these roofs were completely ripped away.

My maternal grandfather, a country solicitor who died before I was born, walked around the streets in his village dressed in a tailcoat, white cravat and clogs stuffed with straw. In 1889 he was in Paris with my grandmother on their honeymoon. I imagine in lavish detail how the city appeared to his eyes, a man who was given to lending money without expecting anything in return. When they were staying in the Hôtel du Louvre, lying in their bed at night, they heard shouting in the streets: 'Help, murder! Help, murder!'

It was in pictures in the *Petit Journal Illustré* that I first saw Paris. I remember a picture of the banquet that was given in 1900 for all the mayors of France; they were shown arriving at the banqueting hall, passing through double ranks of Republican Guards on either side; you could see a country mayor in a blue smock, a mayor who was also a parish priest, a mayor from Brittany in a braided coat, all of them wearing the tricolour sash. Another illustration showed some of these public officers being gently picked up by the police because they were drunk from having been treated too well at the banquet; just as in the time when Baudelaire went home through tragic streets, the town police wore sabres by their sides.

Then I got to know Paris through François Coppée.° Coppée, a good man though often a bad poet, left behind a gentle vision of Paris with an aura all of its own, a Paris inhabited by decent poor people and great nobles who had special uniformed guards to protect their residences.

I must also mention a guidebook, a *Petit guide Diamant* bearing the date 1882; I liked reading the chapter about the theatres. The Acrobats' and Conjurors' theatres were featured, with different kinds of performance being put on in each establishment: tragedies, melodramas, light comedies, supernatural plays, comic operas.

When I made the journey to Paris, I was radiantly happy. At nightfall the train passed through those suburbs that have appeared to me since then with their hidden private chapels and mysterious courtyards where stolen children play sadly; I gazed out at smoke drifting over scorched kitchen gardens.

At my first contact I caught that big city smell that I've

never quite managed to experience since. I walked past a youth hiding a piece of bread in the hollow of his hand and I saw him very briefly inhale the scent of a woman's skin perfumed with violets.

All the people who truly love Paris eventually find their guiding star. I know that in a charming novel, Delobelle shakes his fist at the city, looking at it from the heights of Montmartre; it was here too that Rastignac dreamt of beautiful, sophisticated, exceptional, powerful women, but Balzac was capable of far more besides; on cold nights I like to think that for him, his breath on the windowpane appeared more sumptuous than any opera decor. The coffee aromas were fading and he retired to bed worn out from his Herculean labours, holding Paris in his enormous hand as a child would hold onto a star, making sure not to let it go.

During my Latin Quarter period when I wore a big scruffy hat and my hair long, I went into a little café and I saw a man sitting in front of a glass of blackish liquid and he said, clearly satisfied but without elaborating: 'Oh! There's a poet.' That was all.

There's a secret divine power in you, Paris, like the Dark Sea; sometimes in the evening nothing has been settled, everything is lost and dying, everything is hidden, negotiating with the miraculous night. Who hasn't admired the surprising beauty of uniforms destined for the execution-er's block?

The municipal authorities keep a drinking cup chained to all the Wallace Fountains that are decorated with draped female figures, but at the Hygiene Museum there is an instructional photograph that advises us not to use these cups to quench our thirst.

Perhaps the wanderer lives in a tiny apartment at the furthest reaches of the Rue de Vaugirard; when he gets home, holding his head in his hands, he no longer hears any sound except the very intermittent creak of wood settling in an old wardrobe; to overcome his solitude he perhaps derives some momentary enjoyment from the sheet of white paper on which he sets down his disjointed writing; sickened by the injustice of men, he feels disgust at the voluptuous woman who seems no more than a harpy now.

Translator's Notes

Earth and Sky

The Marshalls' tombs. A section of the Père-Lachaise cemetery contains tombs of the Marshalls in Napoleon's army.

The Sentiments

The allegorical map of the sentiments. La carte de Tendre or *la carte du tendre* was the map of an imaginary country called Tendre invented in the seventeenth century by a group of women at the French court, the *Précieuses*, that was inspired by a novel by Madeleine de Scudery, *Clélie, histoire romaine* (1654). In the map towns, roads and villages represented different stages and aspects of being in love.

La Courtille. Part of the old defensive Fortifications around Paris that were very slowly demolished by pick and shovel after 1919.

Gouffé the bailiff. This was a famous homicide case involving two perpetrators Michel Eyrault and Gabrielle Bompart. In July 1889 the body of a missing Montmartre bailiff Toussaint-Augustin Gouffé was found in a suitcase at Millery, a suburb near Lyons. Gabrielle Bompart lured Gouffé into the Parisian apartment she rented with her accomplice, the swindler Eyrault, enticed him onto the bed and while making love to him wrapped her dressing-gown cord around his neck. Behind a screen Eyrault held a rope attached to a pulley in the ceiling that was designed to hang Gouffé but he jumped out and strangled Gouffé instead. *Le Parisien Illustré, Le Petit Parisien, Le Petit Journal* and other papers carried graphic illustrations showing the bedroom scene and the shocked expression on Gouffé's face.

Solitude

The towers of the Trocadéro. Chaillot was the name of a hill overlooking the Seine. Before the modern Palais de Chaillot was built on the site in 1939 there was the Trocadéro Ethnographic Museum, which opened in 1878 for the Universal Exhibition of that year.

Their single gold louis d'or. A gold 20-franc piece was introduced by Napoleon in 1803, still called the *napoléon* after 1815 but by the mid-nineteenth century silver 5-franc and gold 20-franc coins were given the name *louis* after the king on pre-revolutionary currency. The *louis d'or* has a special significance in nineteenth-century fiction. Those who spoke of *louis d'or* belonged to the world of the moneyed classes, people with income from rents, investments and land.

Monuments

Carpeaux's sculpture. There were delays on the construction of the Opera but in 1867 building started in earnest for the Universal Exhibition of that year when the main façade was unveiled to the public. Carpeaux's lascivious allegorical group called *La Danse* caused a scandal, with one protester even throwing a bottle of ink over the sculpture.

Squares, Gardens, Parks, Arcades

Flatters in the Sahara. Paul Flatters was an officer sent on a mission to the Sahara in 1880 to survey a route for a future French trans-Saharan railway line from Algeria to Niger. In 1881 at Bir el-Garama in southern Algeria the French expedition and their guides, including Flatters, were attacked and killed by Tuaregs.

The Place de la Concorde. An Egyptian obelisk from Luxor (c.1250 BC) is the centrepiece of the Place de la Concorde, erected in 1836 as a neutral symbol under Louis-Philippe, neither too republican nor too monarchist. Eight female statues grouped in pairs representing eight French cities surround the obelisk: Brest and Rouen, Lille and Strasbourg, Lyons and Marseilles, Bordeaux and Nantes. The Chambre des Députés was also located in the square in the Palais-Bourbon.

Churches

Javert. The police inspector in Victor Hugo's novel *Les Misérables*, who relentlessly for years hunts down the escaped prisoner Jean Valjean.

Hospitals and Prisons

He continued working in Vice. La Police des Mœurs dealt with prostitution. From 1802, prostitutes, whether working in brothels or the street, had to put their names on the police register. When the *insoumises* or unregistered prostitutes were arrested they would spend a night at the police station before being made to undergo a medical examination and registration. After the Great War ended many women lost their jobs and some turned to part-time prostitution, giving their professions on registration as shop assistants, seamstresses, laundry workers, housekeepers, florists, bar entertainers, artists' models or street sellers.

Cemeteries

The final stronghold of the Communards. In May 1871 during the last week of the Commune, 147 *Fédérés* (members of the National Guard) who were fighters for the Commune were shot by the Versailles army against the wall at the south-east corner of Père-Lachaise cemetery and their bodies buried in a common grave at the foot of the wall, along with many others. From the late 1880s onwards, the location became a site of memory for the left, symbolising the struggle for liberty and the ideals of the Communards.

The Law Courts

Berryer, Tronchet. In the grand entrance hall of the Palais de Justice there are two large portrait sculptures of famous lawyers, Berryer and Malesherbes. The nineteenth-century lawyer Berryer is flanked by two allegorical figures, Justice and Eloquence. Malesherbes, who defended Louis XVI during the revolution, is flanked by Fidelity with her dog and France who holds out a crown of laurels. This sculpture by Jacques-Edme Dumont dates from the Restauration (1824–5). Typically,

Follain's eye is drawn to the detailed narrative bas relief under the statue of Malesherbes which portrays the king's three lawyers coming to visit him when he was imprisoned (Malesherbes, Tronchet and de Sèze). On the left of the bas relief the king's valet Cléry turns away weeping, hiding his tears with his hand.

Theatres and Cinemas

Von Arnim. The Prussian romantic writer (1781–1831), best known for his adaptation of folksongs with Clemens Brentano, *Des Knaben Wunderhorn*, was also the author of short stories, novels and plays.

Paul Mounet (1847–1922). A famous tragedian at the Comédie Française, or Théatre-Français as it was also known.

The steps of the Ambigu. The Ambigu-Comique, founded in 1769 and demolished in 1966, was rebuilt after a fire in 1827 and could hold 1,900 spectators. Tickets were cheap and it specialised in melodramas, comedies and adaptations of novels with elaborate stage sets.

Gaston Leroux (1868–1927). The author of the supernatural crime novel *Le Fantôme de l'Opéra* (1910). A chandelier falls from the ceiling during a performance, a theatrical technician is found hanged, a 'Phantom of the Opera' demands a payment of 20,000 francs a month and that box number 5 be reserved for him.

Eager children from the poor area nearby. Follain uses the word *zone* to describe this poor area and the part of the Zone in question is near the Saint-Ouen exit from Paris.

Montmartre

Delobelle, Rastignac. In one of Delobelle's novels the narrator shakes his fist at Paris from the heights of Montmartre, an echo of the often-quoted passage on the last page of Balzac's *Père Goriot* (1835), where Rastignac at dusk looks down from the Père-Lachaise cemetery at the city of Paris, described as a humming beehive, and utters his challenge to the city: *À nous deux maintenant!* It's just the two of us now!

The 1912 poets. Guillaume Apollinaire, Blaise Cendrars, Max Jacob, Pierre Mac Orlan and André Salmon were all poets based in Montmartre and admired by Jean Follain, and Jacob and Salmon became his friends. Mac Orlan, André Salmon and Max Jacob all stayed for a while alongside Picasso in the Bateau-Lavoir, a large building with many small rooms and studios on the Rue Ravignan.

It's midnight and Montmartre lights appear ... 'Montmartre', a cabaret song by Jean Lumière. The golden age of Montmartre, from the end of the nineteenth century to 1914, was over by the time Follain arrived in Paris in 1924. Many painters and writers, including Dorgelès, Renoir, Picasso, Fargue, Utrillo, Van Gogh, Dullin, Cendrars and Jacob, took part in cabaret evenings hosted by Frédé Girard at the Lapin Agile, a bar in a two-storeyed house on the Rue des Saules purchased by Aristide Bruant in 1903.

Gaston Couté (1880–1911). An anarchist and pacifist poet and song writer whose work was very popular in cabarets in Montmartre and elsewhere, admired by the urban poet Jehan Rictus. He died of poverty, alcoholism and tuberculosis.

Districts

North African gentlemen. Follain uses the word *sidis* here. When used by North Africans the word equates to *Monsieur* but when used by French people colloquially in the 1930s, to describe travelling pedlars or North African soldiers, the term was offensive.

Quai de Bercy. Until the 1950s this was a vast area of stone-built wine cellars and bonded warehouses on the banks of the Seine. Wine was shipped from regional vineyards to be bottled here at the *cité des vins.* From the 1950s wine was bottled on site at the vineyards and the Quai de Bercy fell into disuse.

Bal Nègre. In the 1920s and 30s a craze for black artists' music, cabaret and jazz from Martinique, Guadeloupe and the US, swept through Paris cabarets and night spots and the Rocher de Cancale, a *guinguette* or simple restaurant where people could dance on the Quai de Bercy, was one such venue. (This is not the gastronomic restaurant of the same name that features in Balzac's novels.) Here Follain uses terms of the time such as *nègre* or *race* which would be offensive in today's language, but without pejorative intent: in his description there is something poignant about the black man's desire to appear white.

The Paris Gates

There was so much hypocrisy. Clashing interest groups meant that the city authorities and government couldn't decide what to do with the Fortifications and the Zone. Various schemes were proposed: a circular boulevard, parks, a railway line. In 1926 social housing was built, HBM (*habitations à bon marché* or good-value housing) for the least well-off and ILM (*immeubles à loyers moyens*) with more modern conveniences: bathrooms, lifts, rubbish chutes.

Battle of Sidi-Brahim. This was a battle lost by French troops in Algeria to Abd El Kader that lasted for three days in September 1845. In 1832 El Kader was chosen by the Algerian tribes as Emir to lead the Algerians against the French; he was an able strategist who defeated the French army on several occasions. The victorious Emir commanded the French bugler Guillaume Rolland to sound the retreat, but he sounded the charge instead.

Le Cavalier Miserey. A novel (1887) by Abel Hermant (1862–1950) that caused a scandal, in part because of its themes of extramarital affairs and homosexuality but mainly because of its unflattering depiction of military life. The captain of Hermant's cavalry regiment had the book burned on a dung-heap at the barracks and Hermant was challenged to fight a duel over it but fortunately his literary friends intervened.

Paris Spirits

'Pull the string and the latch will go up.' *Tire la bobinette et la chevillette cherra* is a repeated phrase in the French version of *Little Red Riding Hood* published by Charles Perrault in 1697, first used by the grandmother and then by the wolf.

Bazar de la Charité. This was a charitable event attended by eminent aristocratic ladies who donated and bought objects in aid of the poor. On 4 May 1897 a cinema projector caught fire and 125 people lost their lives, 118 of them women.

Rollo's sword hilt. Rollo was the first Viking ruler of Normandy. He converted to Christianity and in one legend he is said to have kept holy relics in his sword.

La Goulue. Louise Weber (1866–1929) grew up in Saint-Ouen, a laundry worker who dreamed of becoming a dancer. She worked as a lion tamer for some years until she and her husband were badly mauled by wild animals during a show in 1904. In 1889 at the Moulin Rouge in Montmartre she created an acrobatic dance show that culminated in a dance called *le Chahut*, known abroad as the French can-can. Toulouse Lautrec painted and sketched her many times.

The Maillard girl, Chaumette. La Fille Maillard was Marie-Thérèse Davoux (1766–1818), also known as Mademoiselle Maillard, a singer and dancer who was chosen to represent the Goddess Reason at a revolutionary festival celebrated at Notre-Dame in 1793. Pierre-Gaspard Chaumette (1763–94) was a Revolutionary who became Prosecutor of the Commune of Paris. A famous orator, social reformer and abolitionist, he was an atheist who campaigned for dechristianisation of festivals. He also was against equality between men and women and supported the Terror.

Time and the Hours

The Trône fairground. This ancient fair went through many incarnations in its thousand-year history and took its current name when it moved to the Place du Trône-Renversé in 1812 (renamed Place de la Nation in 1880). It moved to Vincennes outside Paris in 1969.

'The Shadowy Mouth'. *'Ce que dit la bouche d'ombre'* is the final mystical, pantheistic poem in Victor Hugo's collection *Les Contemplations* (1856)

in which he tries to come to terms with the tragic death of his daughter Léopoldine.

Mallarmé's faun. A reference to the poem *'L'après-midi d'un faune'* published in 1876 by the symbolist poet Stéphane Mallarmé with illustrations by Édouard Manet. The poem inspired the orchestral piece by Claude Debussy and the ballet choreographed by Nijinski in 1912.

Holiday Amusements

Pezon. The name Pezon is synonymous with wild animals as there was a dynasty of lion-tamers of that name, originally from Lozère. A bronze statue of the founder, Jean-Baptiste Pezon (1827–97), known as Baptiste Pezon, can be seen at the family tomb in Père-Lachaise cemetery, seated on the back of his lion Brutus. His lioness Bellone features in one of several sketches of his animals made by Toulouse-Lautrec. His son Adrien (Jean-Adrien Pezon, 1871–1920) worked with La Goulue, mentioned in Follain's chapter 'Paris Spirits'. The Pezon referred to here is possibly Baptiste's nephew Gilbert Pezon (1866–1930) or Gilbert's son Jean Pezon (1901–41).

Days of Rioting

The Camelots du Roi were the militant wing of the nationalist monarchist Action Française movement led by Charles Maurras. In his diaries Follain mentions that he does not share their vision of France. On 6 February 1934 at an anti-parliamentary demonstration, the right-wing leagues stormed police barricades around the Chamber of Deputies on the Place de la Concorde. One policeman was killed along with 16 rioters from the extreme right. Over 1,400 were injured, more policemen than rioters.

Near Père-Lachaise cemetery. In the geography of political demonstrations during the 1930s, the Left marched in clearly delineated areas in the east of the city and assembled in the big squares at Nation, Bastille and République as well as at the *Mur des Fédérés* at Père-Lachaise cemetery. The Right marched in the centre of Paris, in the Latin Quarter, Palais Royal, the Champs-Élysées and the Arc de Triomphe. This geography shifted during the decade: on 11 November 1935 the Communists gathered for the first time at the tomb of the unknown soldier under the Arc de Triomphe.

Last Visions

Wallace Fountains. Sir Richard Wallace (1818–90) was a wealthy English philanthropist and art collector who during the Franco-Prussian war in 1870–71 endowed over a hundred drinking fountains throughout Paris for the Parisians who had no access to water. The cast-iron green fountains, designed by Charles Lebourg, are still part of street furniture today. Until the 1950s each fountain had a tin drinking cup attached to it by a chain.

Two Unpublished Extracts

A Day in Paris

Georges Courteline (1858–1929) was author of sketches, pantomimes and comedies popular during the Second Empire.

Veuillot (1813–83) was a self-taught Catholic journalist from a humble background.

Preliminary Notes

Every arrondissement. The arrondissements, or Paris districts, were given their definitive form in 1860.

François Coppée (1842–1908) was an anti-Dreyfusard poet, playwright and dramatist known as *poète des humbles* (poet of the poor). His simple poetry was parodied by Rimbaud but admired by Follain when he was young.

Acknowledgements

Many conversations and books have helped me complete this translation. I am very grateful to Brigitte Lejuez for introducing me to the work of Jean Follain in the first place. I would also like to thank Eamon O'Flaherty for his insights into French history and Frank Wynne for his encouragement of the translation project.

I am indebted to Claire Paulhan's edition of Jean Follain's diaries, *Agendas 1926–1971* (Paris: Seghers, 1993) and to Elodie Bouygues for her in-depth study of Follain's context and development as a writer, not to mention his exhausting literary social life, *Genèse de Jean Follain* (Paris: Classiques Garnier, 2009).

The *Dictionnaire Historique de Paris* edited by Roselyne de Ayala (Paris: Livre de Poche, 2013) was an invaluable guide, as was Colin Jones's history *Paris: Biography of a City* (London: Penguin, 2006).

K.S.